Science 12

Teacher's Guide

CONTENTS

Author: **Alpha Omega Publications**

Editor: Alan Christopherson, M.S.

Alpha Omega Publications®

804 N. 2nd Ave. E., Rock Rapids, IA 51246-1759

OVERVIEW

SCIENCE

Curriculum Overview
Grades 1–12

	Grade 1	Grade 2	Grade 3
LIFEPAC 1	YOU LEARN WITH YOUR EYES • Name and group some colors • Name and group some shapes • Name and group some sizes • Help from what you see	THE LIVING AND NONLIVING • What God created • Rock and seed experiment • God-made objects • Man-made objects	YOU GROW AND CHANGE • Air we breathe • Food for the body • Exercise and rest • You are different
LIFEPAC 2	YOU LEARN WITH YOUR EARS • Sounds of nature and people • How sound moves • Sound with your voice • You make music	PLANTS • How are plants alike • Habitats of plants • Growth of plants • What plants need	PLANTS • Plant parts • Plant growth • Seeds and bulbs • Stems and roots
LIFEPAC 3	MORE ABOUT YOUR SENSES • Sense of smell • Sense of taste • Sense of touch • Learning with my senses	ANIMALS • How are animals alike • How are animals different • What animals need • Noah and the ark	ANIMAL GROWTH AND CHANGE • The environment changes • Animals are different • How animals grow • How animals change
LIFEPAC 4	ANIMALS • What animals eat • Animals for food • Animals for work • Pets to care for	YOU • How are people alike • How are you different • Your family • Your health	YOU ARE WHAT YOU EAT • Food helps your body • Junk foods • Food groups • Good health habits
LIFEPAC 5	PLANTS • Big and small plants • Special plants • Plants for food • House plants	PET AND PLANT CARE • Learning about pets • Caring for pets • Learning about plants • Caring for plants	PROPERTIES OF MATTER • Robert Boyle • States of matter • Physical changes • Chemical changes
LIFEPAC 6	GROWING UP HEALTHY • How plants and animals grow • How your body grows • Eating and sleeping • Exercising	YOUR FIVE SENSES • Your eye • You can smell and hear • Your taste • You can feel	SOUNDS AND YOU • Making sounds • Different sounds • How sounds move • How sounds are heard
LIFEPAC 7	GOD'S BEAUTIFUL WORLD • Types of land • Water places • The weather • Seasons	PHYSICAL PROPERTIES • Colors • Shapes • Sizes • How things feel	TIMES AND SEASONS • The earth rotates • The earth revolves • Time changes • Seasons change
LIFEPAC 8	ALL ABOUT ENERGY • God gives energy • We use energy • Ways to make energy • Ways to save energy	OUR NEIGHBORHOOD • Things not living • Things living • Harm to our world • Caring for our world	ROCKS AND THEIR CHANGES • Forming rocks • Changing rocks • Rocks for buildings • Rock collecting
LIFEPAC 9	MACHINES AROUND YOU • Simple levers • Simple wheels • Inclined planes • Using machines	CHANGES IN OUR WORLD • Seasons • Change in plants • God's love never changes • God's Word never changes	HEAT ENERGY • Sources of heat • Heat energy • Moving heat • Benefits and problems of heat
LIFEPAC 10	WONDERFUL WORLD OF SCIENCE • Using your senses • Using your mind • You love yourself • You love the world	LOOKING AT OUR WORLD • Living things • Nonliving things • Caring for our world • Caring for ourselves	PHYSICAL CHANGES • Change in man • Change in plants • Matter and time • Sound and energy

Grade 4	Grade 5	Grade 6	
PLANTS • Plants and living things • Using plants • Parts of plants • The function of plants	CELLS • Cell composition • Plant and animal cells • Life of cells • Growth of cells	PLANT SYSTEMS • Parts of a plant • Systems of photosynthesis • Transport systems • Regulatory systems	LIFEPAC 1
ANIMALS • Animal structures • Animal behavior • Animal instincts • Man protects animals	PLANTS: LIFE CYCLES • Seed producing plants • Spore producing plants • One-celled plants • Classifying plants	ANIMAL SYSTEMS • Digestive system • Excretory system • Skeletal system • Diseases	LIFEPAC 2
MAN'S ENVIRONMENT • Resources • Balance in nature • Communities • Conservation and preservation	ANIMALS: LIFE CYCLES • Invertebrates • Vertebrates • Classifying animals • Relating function and structure	PLANT AND ANIMAL BEHAVIOR • Animal behavior • Plant behavior • Plant-animal interaction • Balance in nature	LIFEPAC 3
MACHINES • Work and energy • Simple machines • Simple machines together • Complex machines	BALANCE IN NATURE • Needs of life • Dependence on others • Prairie life • Stewardship of nature	MOLECULAR GENETICS • Reproduction • Inheritance • DNA and mutations • Mendel's work	LIFEPAC 4
ELECTRICITY AND MAGNETISM • Electric current • Electric circuits • Magnetic materials • Electricity and magnets	TRANSFORMATION OF ENERGY • Work and energy • Heat energy • Chemical energy • Energy sources	CHEMICAL STRUCTURE • Nature of matter • Periodic Table • Diagrams of atoms • Acids and bases	LIFEPAC 5
CHANGES IN MATTER • Properties of water • Properties of matter • Molecules and atoms • Elements	RECORDS IN ROCK: THE FLOOD • The Biblical account • Before the flood • The flood • After the flood	LIGHT AND SOUND • Sound waves • Light waves • The visible spectrum • Colors	LIFEPAC 6
WEATHER • Causes of weather • Forces of weather • Observing weather • Weather instruments	RECORDS IN ROCK: FOSSILS • Fossil types • Fossil location • Identifying fossils • Reading fossils	MOTION AND ITS MEASUREMENT • Definition of force • Rate of doing work • Laws of motion • Change in motion	LIFEPAC 7
THE SOLAR SYSTEM • Our solar system • The big universe • Sun and planets • Stars and space	RECORDS IN ROCK: GEOLOGY • Features of the earth • Rock of the earth • Forces of the earth • Changes in the earth	SPACESHIP EARTH • Shape of the earth • Rotation and revolution • Eclipses • The solar system	LIFEPAC 8
THE PLANET EARTH • The atmosphere • The hydrosphere • The lithosphere • Rotation and revolution	CYCLES IN NATURE • Properties of matter • Changes in matter • Natural cycles • God's order	ASTRONOMY AND THE STARS • History of astronomy • Investigating stars • Major stars • Constellations	LIFEPAC 9
GOD'S CREATION • Earth and solar system • Matter and weather • Using nature • Conservation	LOOK AHEAD • Plant and animal life • Balance in nature • Biblical records • Records of rock	THE EARTH AND THE UNIVERSE • Plant systems • Animal systems • Physics and chemistry • The earth and stars	LIFEPAC 10

	Grade 7	Grade 8	Grade 9
LIFEPAC 1	WHAT IS SCIENCE • Tools of a scientist • Methods of a scientist • Work of a scientist • Careers in science	SCIENCE AND SOCIETY • Definition of science • History of science • Science today • Science tomorrow	OUR ATOMIC WORLD • Structure of matter • Radioactivity • Atomic nuclei • Nuclear energy
LIFEPAC 2	PERCEIVING THINGS • History of the metric system • Metric units • Advantages of the metric system • Graphing data	STRUCTURE OF MATTER I • Properties of matter • Chemical properties of matter • Atoms and molecules • Elements, compounds, & mixtures	VOLUME, MASS, AND DENSITY • Measure of matter • Volume • Mass • Density
LIFEPAC 3	EARTH IN SPACE I • Ancient stargazing • Geocentric Theory • Copernicus • Tools of astronomy	STRUCTURE OF MATTER II • Changes in matter • Acids • Bases • Salts	PHYSICAL GEOLOGY • Earth structures • Weathering and erosion • Sedimentation • Earth movements
LIFEPAC 4	EARTH IN SPACE II • Solar energy • Planets of the sun • The moon • Eclipses	HEALTH AND NUTRITION • Foods and digestion • Diet • Nutritional diseases • Hygiene	HISTORICAL GEOLOGY • Sedimentary rock • Fossils • Crustal changes • Measuring time
LIFEPAC 5	THE ATMOSPHERE • Layers of the atmosphere • Solar effects • Natural cycles • Protecting the atmosphere	ENERGY I • Kinetic and potential energy • Other forms of energy • Energy conversions • Entropy	BODY HEALTH I • Microorganisms • Bacterial infections • Viral infections • Other infections
LIFEPAC 6	WEATHER • Elements of weather • Air masses and clouds • Fronts and storms • Weather forecasting	ENERGY II • Magnetism • Current and static electricity • Using electricity • Energy sources	BODY HEALTH II • Body defense mechanisms • Treating disease • Preventing disease • Community health
LIFEPAC 7	CLIMATE • Climate and weather • Worldwide climate • Regional climate • Local climate	MACHINES I • Measuring distance • Force • Laws of Newton • Work	ASTRONOMY • Extent of the universe • Constellations • Telescopes • Space explorations
LIFEPAC 8	HUMAN ANATOMY I • Cell structure and function • Skeletal and muscle systems • Skin • Nervous system	MACHINES II • Friction • Levers • Wheels and axles • Inclined planes	OCEANOGRAPHY • History of oceanography • Research techniques • Geology of the ocean • Properties of the ocean
LIFEPAC 9	HUMAN ANATOMY II • Respiratory system • Circulatory system • Digestive system • Endocrine system	BALANCE IN NATURE • Photosynthesis • Food • Natural cycles • Balance in nature	SCIENCE AND TOMORROW • The land • Waste and ecology • Industry and energy • New frontiers
LIFEPAC 10	CAREERS IN SCIENCE • Scientists at work • Astronomy • Meteorology • Medicine	SCIENCE AND TECHNOLOGY • Basic science • Physical science • Life science • Vocations in science	SCIENTIFIC APPLICATIONS • Measurement • Practical health • Geology and astronomy • Solving problems

Grade 10	Grade 11	Grade 12	
TAXONOMY • History of taxonomy • Binomial nomenclature • Classification • Taxonomy	INTRODUCTION TO CHEMISTRY • Metric units and instrumentation • Observation and hypothesizing • Scientific notation • Careers in chemistry	KINEMATICS • Scalars and vectors • Length measurement • Acceleration • Fields and models	LIFEPAC 1
BASIS OF LIFE • Elements and molecules • Properties of compounds • Chemical reactions • Organic compounds	BASIC CHEMICAL UNITS • Alchemy • Elements • Compounds • Mixtures	DYNAMICS • Newton's Laws of Motion • Gravity • Circular motion • Kepler's Laws of Motion	LIFEPAC 2
MICROBIOLOGY • The microscope • Protozoan • Algae • Microorganisms	GASES AND MOLES • Kinetic theory • Gas laws • Combined gas law • Moles	WORK AND ENERGY • Mechanical energy • Conservation of energy • Power and efficiency • Heat energy	LIFEPAC 3
CELLS • Cell theories • Examination of the cell • Cell design • Cells in organisms	ATOMIC MODELS • Historical models • Modern atomic structure • Periodic Law • Nuclear reactions	WAVES • Energy transfers • Reflection and refraction of waves • Diffraction and interference • Sound waves	LIFEPAC 4
PLANTS: GREEN FACTORIES • The plant cell • Anatomy of the plant • Growth and function of plants • Plants and people	CHEMICAL FORMULAS • Ionic charges • Electronegativity • Chemical bonds • Molecular shape	LIGHT • Speed of light • Mirrors • Lenses • Models of light	LIFEPAC 5
HUMAN ANATOMY AND PHYSIOLOGY • Digestive and excretory system • Respiratory and circulatory system • Skeletal and muscular system • Body control systems	CHEMICAL REACTIONS • Detecting reactions • Energy changes • Reaction rates • Equilibriums	STATIC ELECTRICITY • Nature of charges • Transfer of charges • Electric fields • Electric potential	LIFEPAC 6
INHERITANCE • Gregor Mendel's experiments • Chromosomes and heredity • Molecular genetics • Human genetics	EQUILIBRIUM SYSTEMS • Solutions • Solubility equilibriums • Acid-base equilibriums • Redox equilibriums	CURRENT ELECTRICITY • Electromotive force • Electron flow • Resistance • Circuits	LIFEPAC 7
CELL DIVISION & REPRODUCTION • Mitosis and meiosis • Asexual reproduction • Sexual reproduction • Plant reproduction	HYDROCARBONS • Organic compounds • Carbon atoms • Carbon bonds • Saturated and unsaturated	MAGNETISM • Fields • Forces • Electromagnetism • Electron beams	LIFEPAC 8
ECOLOGY & ENERGY • Ecosystems • Communities and habitats • Pollution • Energy	CARBON CHEMISTRY • Saturated and unsaturated • Reaction types • Oxygen groups • Nitrogen groups	ATOMIC AND NUCLEAR PHYSICS • Electromagnetic radiation • Quantum theory • Nuclear theory • Nuclear reaction	LIFEPAC 9
APPLICATIONS OF BIOLOGY • Principles of experimentation • Principles of reproduction • Principles of life • Principles of ecology	ATOMS TO HYDROCARBONS • Atoms and molecules • Chemical bonding • Chemical systems • Organic chemistry	KINEMATICS TO NUCLEAR PHYSICS • Mechanics • Wave motion • Electricity • Modern physics	LIFEPAC 10

LIFEPAC

MANAGEMENT

STRUCTURE OF THE LIFEPAC CURRICULUM

The LIFEPAC curriculum is conveniently structured to provide one teacher handbook containing teacher support material with answer keys and ten student worktexts for each subject at grade levels two through twelve. The worktext format of the LIFEPACs allows the student to read the textual information and complete workbook activities all in the same booklet. The easy to follow LIFEPAC numbering system lists the grade as the first number(s) and the last two digits as the number of the series. For example, the Language Arts LIFEPAC at the 6th grade level, 5th book in the series would be LA 605.

Each LIFEPAC is divided into 3 to 5 sections and begins with an introduction or overview of the booklet as well as a series of specific learning objectives to give a purpose to the study of the LIFEPAC. The introduction and objectives are followed by a vocabulary section which may be found at the beginning of each section at the lower levels, at the beginning of the LIFEPAC in the middle grades, or in the glossary at the high school level. Vocabulary words are used to develop word recognition and should not be confused with the spelling words introduced later in the LIFEPAC. The student should learn all vocabulary words before working the LIFEPAC sections to improve comprehension, retention, and reading skills.

Each activity or written assignment has a number for easy identification, such as 1.1. The first number corresponds to the LIFEPAC section and the number to the right of the decimal is the number of the activity.

Teacher checkpoints, which are essential to maintain quality learning, are found at various locations throughout the LIFEPAC. The teacher should check 1) neatness of work and penmanship, 2) quality of understanding (tested with a short oral quiz), 3) thoroughness of answers (complete sentences and paragraphs, correct spelling, etc.), 4) completion of activities (no blank spaces), and 5) accuracy of answers as compared to the answer key (all answers correct).

The self test questions are also number coded for easy reference. For example, 2.015 means that this is the 15th question in the self test of Section II. The first number corresponds to the LIFEPAC section, the zero indicates that it is a self test question, and the number to the right of the zero the question number.

The LIFEPAC test is packaged at the centerfold of each LIFEPAC. It should be removed and put aside before giving the booklet to the student for study.

Answer and test keys have the same numbering system as the LIFEPACs and appear at the back of this handbook. The student may be given access to the answer keys (not the test keys) under teacher supervision so that he can score his own work.

A thorough study of the Curriculum Overview by the teacher before instruction begins is essential to the success of the student. The teacher should become familiar with expected skill mastery and understand how these grade level skills fit into the overall skill development of the curriculum. The teacher should also preview the objectives that appear at the beginning of each LIFEPAC for additional preparation and planning.

TEST SCORING and GRADING

Answer keys and test keys give examples of correct answers. They convey the idea, but the student may use many ways to express a correct answer. The teacher should check for the essence of the answer, not for the exact wording. Many questions are high level and require thinking and creativity on the part of the student. Each answer should be scored based on whether or not the main idea written by the student matches the model example. "Any Order" or "Either Order" in a key indicates that no particular order is necessary to be correct.

Most self tests and LIFEPAC tests at the lower elementary levels are scored at 1 point per question; however, the upper levels may have a point system awarding 2 to 5 points for various questions. Further, the total test points will vary; they may not always equal 100 points. They may be 78, 85, 100, 105, etc.

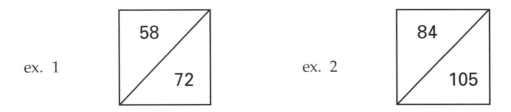

ex. 1   58 / 72   ex. 2   84 / 105

A score box similar to ex.1 above is located at the end of each self test and on the front of the LIFEPAC test. The bottom score, 72, represents the total number of points possible on the test. The upper score, 58, represents the number of points your student will need to receive an 80% or passing grade. If you wish to establish the exact percentage that your student has achieved, find the total points of his correct answers and divide it by the bottom number (in this case 72.) For example, if your student has a point total of 65, divide 65 by 72 for a grade of 90%. Referring to ex. 2, on a test with a total of 105 possible points, the student would have to receive a minimum of 84 correct points for an 80% or passing grade. If your student has received 93 points, simply divide the 93 by 105 for a percentage grade of 89%. Students who receive a score below 80% should review the LIFEPAC and retest using the appropriate Alternate Test found in the Teacher's Guide.

The following is a guideline to assign letter grades for completed LIFEPACs based on a maximum total score of 100 points.

LIFEPAC Test = 60% of the Total Score (or percent grade)
Self Test   = 25% of the Total Score (average percent of self tests)
Reports   = 10% or 10* points per LIFEPAC
Oral Work   = 5% or 5* points per LIFEPAC
*Determined by the teacher's subjective evaluation of the student's daily work.

Example:

LIFEPAC Test Score	=	92%	92 x .60	=	55 points
Self Test Average	=	90%	90 x .25	=	23 points
Reports				=	8 points
Oral Work				=	4 points

TOTAL POINTS = 90 points

Grade Scale based on point system:

100	–	94	=	A
93	–	86	=	B
85	–	77	=	C
76	–	70	=	D
Below		70	=	F

TEACHER HINTS and STUDYING TECHNIQUES

LIFEPAC Activities are written to check the level of understanding of the preceding text. The student may look back to the text as necessary to complete these activities; however, a student should never attempt to do the activities without reading (studying) the text first. Self tests and LIFEPAC tests are never open book tests.

Language arts activities (skill integration) often appear within other subject curriculum. The purpose is to give the student an opportunity to test his skill mastery outside of the context in which it was presented.

Writing complete answers (paragraphs) to some questions is an integral part of the LIFEPAC Curriculum in all subjects. This builds communication and organization skills, increases understanding and retention of ideas, and helps enforce good penmanship. Complete sentences should be encouraged for this type of activity. Obviously, single words or phrases do not meet the intent of the activity, since multiple lines are given for the response.

Review is essential to student success. Time invested in review where review is suggested will be time saved in correcting errors later. Self tests, unlike the section activities, are closed book. This procedure helps to identify weaknesses before they become too great to overcome. Certain objectives from self tests are cumulative and test previous sections; therefore, good preparation for a self test must include all material studied up to that testing point.

The following procedure checklist has been found to be successful in developing good study habits in the LIFEPAC curriculum.

1. Read the introduction and Table of Contents.
2. Read the objectives.
3. Recite and study the entire vocabulary (glossary) list.
4. Study each section as follows:
    a. Read the introduction and study the section objectives.
    b. Read all the text for the entire section, but answer none of the activities.
    c. Return to the beginning of the section and memorize each vocabulary word and definition.
    d. Reread the section, complete the activities, check the answers with the answer key, correct all errors, and have the teacher check.
    e. Read the self test but do not answer the questions.
    f. Go to the beginning of the first section and reread the text and answers to the activities up to the self test you have not yet done.
    g. Answer the questions to the self test without looking back.
    h. Have the self test checked by the teacher.
    i. Correct the self test and have the teacher check the corrections.
    j. Repeat steps a–i for each section.

5. Use the SQ3R* method to prepare for the LIFEPAC test.
6. Take the LIFEPAC test as a closed book test.
7. LIFEPAC tests are administered and scored under direct teacher supervision. Students who receive scores below 80% should review the LIFEPAC using the SQ3R* study method and take the Alternate Test located in the Teacher Handbook. The final test grade may be the grade on the Alternate Test or an average of the grades from the original LIFEPAC test and the Alternate Test.

   *SQ3R: Scan the whole LIFEPAC.
   Question yourself on the objectives.
   Read the whole LIFEPAC again.
   Recite through an oral examination.
   Review weak areas.

GOAL SETTING and SCHEDULES

Each school must develop its own schedule, because no single set of procedures will fit every situation. The following is an example of a daily schedule that includes the five LIFEPAC subjects as well as time slotted for special activities.

Possible Daily Schedule

8:15	–	8:25	Pledges, prayer, songs, devotions, etc.
8:25	–	9:10	Bible
9:10	–	9:55	Language Arts
9:55	–	10:15	Recess (juice break)
10:15	–	11:00	Mathematics
11:00	–	11:45	Social Studies
11:45	–	12:30	Lunch, recess, quiet time
12:30	–	1:15	Science
1:15	–		Drill, remedial work, enrichment*

*Enrichment: Computer time, physical education, field trips, fun reading, games and puzzles, family business, hobbies, resource persons, guests, crafts, creative work, electives, music appreciation, projects.

Basically, two factors need to be considered when assigning work to a student in the LIFEPAC curriculum.

The first is time. An average of 45 minutes should be devoted to each subject, each day. Remember, this is only an average. Because of extenuating circumstances a student may spend only 15 minutes on a subject one day and the next day spend 90 minutes on the same subject.

The second factor is the number of pages to be worked in each subject. A single LIFEPAC is designed to take 3 to 4 weeks to complete. Allowing about 3-4 days for LIFEPAC introduction, review, and tests, the student has approximately 15 days to complete the LIFEPAC pages. Simply take the number of pages in the LIFEPAC, divide it by 15 and you will have the number of pages that must be completed on a daily basis to keep the student on schedule. For example, a LIFEPAC containing 45 pages will require 3 completed pages per day. Again, this is only an average. While working a 45 page LIFEPAC, the student may complete only 1 page the first day if the text has a lot of activities or reports, but go on to complete 5 pages the next day.

Long range planning requires some organization. Because the traditional school year originates in the early fall of one year and continues to late spring of the following year, a calendar should be devised that covers this period of time. Approximate beginning and completion dates can be noted on the calendar as well as special occasions such as holidays, vacations and birthdays. Since each LIFEPAC takes 3-4 weeks or eighteen days to complete, it should take about 180 school days to finish a set of ten LIFEPACs. Starting at the beginning school date, mark off eighteen school days on the calendar and that will become the targeted completion date for the first LIFEPAC. Continue marking the calendar until you have established dates for the remaining nine LIFEPACs making adjustments for previously noted holidays and vacations. If all five subjects are being used, the ten established target dates should be the same for the LIFEPACs in each subject.

FORMS

The sample weekly lesson plan and student grading sheet forms are included in this section as teacher support materials and may be duplicated at the convenience of the teacher.

The student grading sheet is provided for those who desire to follow the suggested guidelines for assignment of letter grades found on page 3 of this section. The student's self test scores should be posted as percentage grades. When the LIFEPAC is completed the teacher should average the self test grades, multiply the average by .25 and post the points in the box marked self test points. The LIFEPAC percentage grade should be multiplied by .60 and posted. Next, the teacher should award and post points for written reports and oral work. A report may be any type of written work assigned to the student whether it is a LIFEPAC or additional learning activity. Oral work includes the student's ability to respond orally to questions which may or may not be related to LIFEPAC activities or any type of oral report assigned by the teacher. The points may then be totaled and a final grade entered along with the date that the LIFEPAC was completed.

The Student Record Book which was specifically designed for use with the Alpha Omega curriculum provides space to record weekly progress for one student over a nine week period as well as a place to post self test and LIFEPAC scores. The Student Record Books are available through the current Alpha Omega catalog; however, unlike the enclosed forms these books are not for duplication and should be purchased in sets of four to cover a full academic year.

WEEKLY LESSON PLANNER

Week of:

	Subject	Subject	Subject	Subject
Monday				
	Subject	Subject	Subject	Subject
Tuesday				
	Subject	Subject	Subject	Subject
Wednesday				
	Subject	Subject	Subject	Subject
Thursday				
	Subject	Subject	Subject	Subject
Friday				

21

WEEKLY LESSON PLANNER

Week of:

Subject	Subject	Subject	Subject
Monday			

Subject	Subject	Subject	Subject
Tuesday			

Subject	Subject	Subject	Subject
Wednesday			

Subject	Subject	Subject	Subject
Thursday			

Subject	Subject	Subject	Subject
Friday			

Student Name _____   Year _____

Bible

LP #	Self Test Scores by Sections 1	2	3	4	5	Self Test Points	LIFEPAC Test	Oral Points	Report Points	Final Grade	Date
01											
02											
03											
04											
05											
06											
07											
08											
09											
10											

History & Geography

LP #	Self Test Scores by Sections 1	2	3	4	5	Self Test Points	LIFEPAC Test	Oral Points	Report Points	Final Grade	Date
01											
02											
03											
04											
05											
06											
07											
08											
09											
10											

Language Arts

LP #	Self Test Scores by Sections 1	2	3	4	5	Self Test Points	LIFEPAC Test	Oral Points	Report Points	Final Grade	Date
01											
02											
03											
04											
05											
06											
07											
08											
09											
10											

Student Name _____   Year _____

Mathematics

LP #	Self Test Scores by Sections 1	2	3	4	5	Self Test Points	LIFEPAC Test	Oral Points	Report Points	Final Grade	Date
01											
02											
03											
04											
05											
06											
07											
08											
09											
10											

Science

LP #	Self Test Scores by Sections 1	2	3	4	5	Self Test Points	LIFEPAC Test	Oral Points	Report Points	Final Grade	Date
01											
02											
03											
04											
05											
06											
07											
08											
09											
10											

Spelling/Electives

LP #	Self Test Scores by Sections 1	2	3	4	5	Self Test Points	LIFEPAC Test	Oral Points	Report Points	Final Grade	Date
01											
02											
03											
04											
05											
06											
07											
08											
09											
10											

TEACHER

NOTES

INSTRUCTIONS FOR SCIENCE

The LIFEPAC curriculum from grades two through twelve is structured so that the daily instructional material is written directly into the LIFEPACs. The student is encouraged to read and follow this instructional material in order to develop independent study habits. The teacher should introduce the LIFEPAC to the student, set a required completion schedule, complete teacher checks, be available for questions regarding both content and procedures, administer and grade tests, and develop additional learning activities as desired. Teachers working with several students may schedule their time so that students are assigned to a quiet work activity when it is necessary to spend instructional time with one particular student.

The Teacher Notes section of the Teacher's Guide lists the required or suggested materials for the LIFEPACs and provides additional learning activities for the students. The materials section refers only to LIFEPAC materials and does not include materials which may be needed for the additional activities. Additional learning activities provide a change from the daily school routine, encourage the student's interest in learning and may be used as a reward for good study habits.

If you have limited facilities and are not able to perform all the experiments contained in the LIFEPAC curriculum, the Science Project List for grades 3-12 may be a useful tool for you. This list prioritizes experiments into three categories: those essential to perform, those which should be performed as time and facilities permit, and those not essential for mastery of LIFEPACs. Of course, for complete understanding of concepts and student participation in the curriculum, all experiments should be performed whenever practical. Materials for the experiments are shown in Teacher Notes—Materials Needed.

Science Projects List

Key

(1) = Those essential to perform for basic understanding of scientific principles.

(2) = Those which should be performed as time permits.

(3) = Those not essential for mastery of LIFEPACs.

S = Equipment needed for home school or Christian school lab.

E = Explanation or demonstration by instructor may replace student or class lab work.

H = Suitable for homework or for home school students. (No lab equipment needed.)

Science 1201

pp	4	(1)	S
	12	(1)	S
	18	(1)	S
	30	(1)	S
	34	(2)	S
	36	(2)	H

Science 1202

pp	6	(1)	S
	27	(1)	S
	34	(1)	S
	36	(1)	S
	44	(1)	H

Science 1203

pp	13	(1)	S
	19	(1)	H
	28	(2)	S

Science 1204

pp	2	(1)	H
	4	(1)	H
	7	(1)	S
	8	(1)	H

10	(3)	S
14	(1)	S
15	(1)	H
16	(1)	S
18	(1)	H
20	(1)	S
22	(1)	H
24	(1)	H
25	(1)	S
33	(1)	S
34	(1)	S
35	(1)	S

Science 1205

pp	4	(1)	H
	7	(1)	H
	9	(1)	S
	12	(1)	S
	14	(1)	H
	19	(1)	S
	22	(1)	S
	26	(1)	S
	33	(2)	S
	36	(2)	S

Science 1206

pp	6	(3)	S

Science 1207

None

Science 1208

pp	5	(2)	S
	14	(1)	S

Science 1209

None

Science 1210

None

MATERIALS NEEDED

Section I

Page 4   screw, paper straw, 2 microscope slides, needle, ruler, razor blade, wood block, tongue depressor, clothespin, paper

Section II

Page 12   100-cc graduated cylinder, 50-cc graduated cylinder, large tray, 2 eyedroppers, talcum powder, oleic acid, alcohol, meter stick

Section III

Page 18   battery ($1\frac{1}{2}$ V), C-clamp, percussion timer, waxed timer tape, ruler

Section IV

Page 30   timer, tape, ruler, battery, C-clamp

Section V

Page 34   15 to 30 thermometers, 3 acetate sheets

Page 36   roll of adding machine tape, meter stick

ADDITIONAL ACTIVITIES
The following activities may be reproduced as student worksheets.

Section I Units, Scalars, and Vectors

1. Calculate $1.8 \cdot 10^4$ times $4 \cdot 10^{-6}$ divided by $3 \cdot 10^2$.

2. Calculate $7 \cdot 10^{-2}$ times $4 \cdot 10^{-3}$ divided by $5 \cdot 10^{-7}$.

3. Express $5 \cdot 10^5$ m in km.

4. Express $3.2 \cdot 10^2$ m in cm.

5. Add these vectors.

$$\vec{A} \ - \ \vec{B} \ + \ \vec{C} \ - \ \vec{D}$$

6. Find the vertical and horizontal components of C.

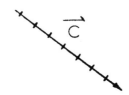

30

Section II Measurement of Length

   1. If you travel 3 blocks north and 4 blocks east, calculate the distance traveled and the displacement.

   2. An object 4 cm wide, 5 cm long, and 2 cm high has a mass of 8 g. a) Find the area of the base. b) Find the volume. c) Calculate the density.

Section III Rate of Length Change

City B is 80 miles north of City A but travel by road is 100 miles.
It takes 2 hours to travel by car from B to A. a) Calculate the
speed. b) Calculate the velocity.

Section IV Rate of Velocity

   1. Calculate the acceleration of an object traveling at 30 $\frac{ft.}{sec.}$ in a radius of 9 ft.

   2. A car traveling at 60 $\frac{m}{sec.}$ NE changes to 70 $\frac{m}{sec.}$ NE in 5 seconds. Calculate the acceleration.

   3. An object falls from rest under the influence of gravity for 4 seconds. Calculate the distance it falls in meters and feet.

ADDITIONAL ACTIVITIES, Answer Key

Section I Units, Scalars, and Vectors

1. $\dfrac{(1.8 \cdot 10^4)(4 \cdot 10^{-6})}{3 \cdot 10^2} = \dfrac{(1.8)(4)}{3} \cdot 10^{4-6-2}$

$$= 2.4 \cdot 10^{-4}$$

2. $\dfrac{(7 \cdot 10^{-2})(4 \cdot 10^{-3})}{5 \cdot 10^{-7}} = \dfrac{(7)(4)}{5} \cdot 10^{-2-3-(-7)}$

$$\dfrac{28}{5} \cdot 10^2 = 5.6 \cdot 10^2$$

3. $5 \cdot 10^5$ m $= 5 \cdot 10^2 \cdot 10^3$ m $= 5 \cdot 10^2$ km

$$= 500 \text{ km}$$

4. $3.2 \cdot 10^2$ m $= 3.2 \cdot 10^2 \cdot (10^{+2} \cdot 10^{-2})$ m

$$= 3.2 \cdot 10^2 \cdot 10^2 \text{ cm}$$

$$= 3.2 \cdot 10^4 \text{ cm}$$

5.

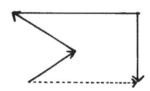

6.

Section II Measurement of Length

1. distance is 3 + 4 blocks = 7 blocks

displacement is 3 + 4 = 5

2. a. A = $l \cdot w$ 4 cm $\cdot$ 5 cm = 20 cm^2
    b. V = $l \cdot w \cdot h$ 4 cm $\cdot$ 5 cm $\cdot$ 2 cm = 40 cm^3

c. Density $= \dfrac{\text{Mass}}{\text{Volume}} = \dfrac{8 \text{ g}}{40 \text{ cm}^3} = \dfrac{5 \text{ g}}{\text{cc}}$

Section III Rate of Length Change

1. a. $S = \dfrac{\Delta d}{\Delta t} = \dfrac{100 \text{ mi.}}{2 \text{ hr.}} = 50 \text{ mph}$

    b. $v = \dfrac{\Delta d}{\Delta t} = \dfrac{80 \text{ mi. north}}{2 \text{ hr.}} = 40 \text{ mph, north}$

Section IV Rate of Velocity

1. a. $\dfrac{v^2}{R} = \dfrac{(30 \frac{\text{ft.}}{\text{sec.}})(30 \frac{\text{ft.}}{\text{sec.}})}{9 \text{ ft.}} = \dfrac{900 \frac{\text{ft.}^2}{\text{sec.}^2}}{9 \text{ ft.}}$

    $= 100 \dfrac{\text{ft.}}{\text{sec.}^2}$,   direction is always toward the center.

2. $a = \dfrac{\Delta v}{\Delta t} = \dfrac{70 \frac{\text{m}}{\text{sec.}} - 60 \frac{\text{m}}{\text{sec.}}, \text{ NE}}{5 \text{ sec.}}$

    $= \dfrac{10 \frac{\text{m}}{\text{sec.}}}{5 \text{ sec.}}$, NE $= 2 \dfrac{\text{m}}{\text{sec.}^2}$, NE

3. $d = \frac{1}{2}gt^2 = \frac{1}{2}(32 \frac{\text{ft.}}{\text{sec.}^2})(4 \text{ sec.})^2$

    $= 16 \cdot 16 \dfrac{\text{ft.}}{\text{sec.}^2}$

    $= 256 \dfrac{\text{ft.}}{\text{sec.}^2}$

    $d = \frac{1}{2}gt^2 = \frac{1}{2}(9.8 \frac{\text{m}}{\text{sec.}^2})(4 \text{ sec.})^2$

    $= (4.9)(16) \dfrac{\text{m}}{\text{sec.}^2}$

    $= 78.4 \dfrac{\text{m}}{\text{sec.}^2}$

MATERIALS NEEDED

Section I

Page 6   percussion timer, two C-clamps, tape, cart, meter stick, wood bumper, balance, several masses, heavy rubber bands, plastic bags, masking tape

Section II

None

Section III

Page 27   glass tube, string, 2 stoppers, alligator clip, paper clip, 10 washers, stop watch

Section IV

Page 34   2 carts, 2 clamps, table, 2 boards, meter sticks, assorted standard masses

Page 36   ramp, 2 steel spheres, grooved ruler, 4 sheets carbon paper, 4 sheets plain paper, meter stick

Section V

Page 44   pencil, ruler

ADDITIONAL ACTIVITIES
The following activities may be reproduced as student worksheets.

Section I Newton's First and Second Laws of Motion

1. A ball of 0.5 kg attains a speed of 10 $\frac{m}{sec.}$ after being struck. Calculate its momentum and the impulse it received.

2. If the force that set the ball in motion was 100 N, calculate the impact time.

Section II Gravity

If an object weighs 320 pounds on the surface of the earth, how much would it weigh 4 earth radii away?

Section III Uniform Circular Motion

1. A stone tied to a string is swung in a circle with a speed of $15 \frac{m}{sec.}$ in an arc of 5 m. Calculate the centripetal acceleration.

2. If the stone has a mass of .3 kg, calculate the centripetal force.

Section IV Newton's Third Law of Motion

Two boys of 30 kg and 40 kg push off from each other on ice skates. If the lighter boy moves at 0.8 $\frac{m}{sec.}$, how fast does the 40 kg boy move?

Section V   Kepler's Laws of Planetary Motion

Planet A is 1 A.U. from the sun and takes 1 year to orbit.
Planet B is 3 A.U. from the sun. Approximately how long
does it take Planet B to orbit the sun?

ADDITIONAL ACTIVITIES, Answer Key

Section I Newton's First and Second Laws of Motion

1. momentum $= \dfrac{m}{v} = (0.5 \text{ kg})(10 \dfrac{m}{\text{sec.}})$

    $= 5 \text{ kg} \cdot \dfrac{m}{\text{sec.}}$

    Impulse $=$ momentum $= 5 \text{ kg} \cdot \dfrac{m}{\text{sec.}}$

2. Impulse $= F\Delta t = 5 \text{ kg} \cdot \dfrac{m}{\text{sec.}}$

    $\Delta t = \dfrac{5 \text{ kg} \cdot \dfrac{m}{\text{sec.}}}{F} = \dfrac{5 \text{ kg} \cdot \dfrac{m}{\text{sec.}}}{100 \text{ N}} = .05 \text{ sec.}$

    $\left[\dfrac{\dfrac{Kg \cdot m}{\text{sec.}}}{N} = \dfrac{\dfrac{Kg \cdot m}{\text{sec.}}}{Kg \dfrac{m^2}{\text{sec.}^2}} \right]$

Section II Gravity

1. Weight $= F = \dfrac{Gm_1 m_2}{R} = \dfrac{Gm_E m_o}{(4R)^2} = \dfrac{Gm_E m_o}{R^2} = \dfrac{1}{16}$

    $= (320 \text{ lb})(\dfrac{1}{16}) = 20 \text{ lb.}$

Section III Uniform Circular Motion

1. $a = \dfrac{v^2}{R} = \dfrac{(15 \dfrac{m}{\text{sec.}})(15 \dfrac{m}{\text{sec.}})}{5 \text{ m}} = 45 \dfrac{m}{\text{sec.}^2}$

2. $F = ma = (.3 \text{ kg})(45 \dfrac{m}{\text{sec.}^2})$

    $= 15 \text{ kg} \dfrac{m}{\text{sec.}^2} = 15 \text{ N}$

Section IV Newton's Third Law of Motion

1. $m_1 v_1 = m_2 v_2$

    $(30 \text{ kg})(0.8 \dfrac{m}{\text{sec.}}) = (40 \text{ kg})(v_2)$

    $v_2 = \dfrac{(30 \text{ kg})(0.8 \dfrac{m}{\text{sec.}})}{40 \text{ kg}}$

    $v_2 = 0.6 \dfrac{m}{\text{sec.}}$

Section V   Kepler's Laws of Planetary Motion

1. $\dfrac{T_A{}^2}{D_A{}^3} = \dfrac{T_B{}^2}{D_B{}^3} = \dfrac{(1 \text{ yr.})^2}{(1 \text{ AU})^3} = \dfrac{T_B{}^2}{(3 \text{ AU})^3}$

   $1 \cdot T_B{}^2 = 1 \cdot 27 \text{ yr.}^2$

   T_B = approximately 5 yr.

MATERIALS NEEDED

    Section I

       None

    Section II

       Page 13 brick, twine, percussion timer, battery, ring stand, meter stick, guy wires, several clamps, tape

       Page 19 meter stick, string, weights

    Section III

       Page 28 aluminum calorimeter, analytical balance, Celsius thermometer, paper towel, cardboard, crushed ice

ADDITIONAL ACTIVITIES
The following activities may be reproduced as student worksheets.

Section I Type and Source of Energy

A 2 kg mass is lifted to a height of 5 m. What is the potential energy?

Section II Conservation of Energy, Power, and Efficiency

1. A 2 kg mass is dropped from 5 m. At what speed does it hit the ground?

2. A winch lifts a 10 kg mass 2 m in 1 second. Another winch lifts the same mass 2 m in 2 seconds. Calculate the power exerted by each winch.

3. If the input work of an engine is 900 joules and the output is 300 joules, what is the efficiency of the engine?

Section III Heat Energy

1. Calculate the efficiency of a steam engine whose input
    temperature is 400°K as steam enters the turbine and
    exhausts at 360°K.

2. Two kg of iron (C = 0.11 $\frac{kcal}{kg - °C}$) is heated from 50°C to
    150°C. Calculate the heat energy used in the process.

3. If 44 kcal of heat is needed to raise the temperature of 4 kg
    of a material by 50°C, determine the material used. Find the
    specific heat and then use the chart on page 24 of the LIFEPAC
    to identify the material.

ADDITIONAL LEARNING ACTIVITIES, Answer Key

Section I Type and Source of Energy

1. P.E. $= mgh = 2$ kg $(9.8 \frac{m}{sec.^2})(5$ m$)$

    $= 98$ kg $\frac{m^2}{sec.^2} = 98$ j

Section II Conservation of Energy, Power, and Efficiency

1. K.E. $= \frac{1}{2}mv^2 = $ P.E. $= 985$

    $= \frac{1}{2}(2$ kg$)v^2 = 98$ j

    $v^2 = 98 \frac{m^2}{sec.^2}$

    $v = 9.9 \frac{m}{sec.}$

2. a) $P = \frac{\Delta E}{\Delta t} = \frac{mgh}{\Delta t} = \frac{(10 \text{ kg})(9.8 \frac{m}{sec.^2})(2 \text{ m})}{1 \text{ sec.}}$

        $= 196 \frac{j}{sec.} = 196$ watts

    b) $P = \frac{\Delta E}{\Delta t} = \frac{mgh}{\Delta t} = \frac{(10 \text{ kg})(9.8 \frac{m}{sec.^2})(2 \text{ m})}{2 \text{ sec.}}$

        $= 98 \frac{j}{sec.} = 98$ watts

3. Efficiency $= \frac{\text{output work}}{\text{input work}} \cdot 100\%$

    $= \frac{300 \text{ j}}{900 \text{ j}} \cdot 100\% = 33\frac{1}{3}\%$

Section III Heat Energy

1. Efficiency $= \frac{T_h - T_c}{T_h} \cdot 100\% = \frac{400°K - 360°K}{400°K} \cdot 100\%$

    $= \frac{40 \text{ K}}{400 \text{ K}} \cdot 100\%$

    $= 10\%$

2. Heat = mCΔt

$$= (2 \text{ kg})(0.11 \frac{\text{kcal}}{\text{kg} - °\text{C}})(100°\text{C})$$

$$= 22 \text{ kcal}$$

3. Heat = mCΔt

$$44 \text{ kcal} = (4 \text{ kg})(\text{C})(50°\text{C})$$

$$\frac{44 \text{ kcal}}{200 \text{ kg} - °\text{C}} = \text{C}$$

$$\frac{.22 \text{ kcal}}{\text{kg} - °\text{C}} = \text{C}; \text{ material is aluminum}$$

MATERIALS NEEDED

Section I

Page 2   Slinky®

Page 4   Slinky®, stop watch, meter stick

Page 8   Slinky®

Page 10   flexible wire strip, metal rods with weighted ends

Section II

Page 14   ripple tank, light source, white paper, protractor, paraffin blocks, electrical wave generator, dowel

Page 16   complete ripple tank apparatus, washers, glass plate

Page 18   Slinky®, coil spring

Page 20   complete ripple tank apparatus

Page 22   Slinky®

Page 24   Slinky®

Page 25   complete ripple tank apparatus

Section III

Page 34   complete ripple tank apparatus

Page 35   speed of sound apparatus, tuning fork, thermometer

ADDITIONAL ACTIVITIES
    The following activities may be reproduced as student worksheets.

Section I Energy Transfer

1. A tuning fork emits a wave length of 3 m. If the speed of sound is 330 $\frac{m}{sec.}$, calculate the frequency and period of the wave.

2. A water wave at high tide crests one meter above the high-water mark. A wave is observed every two seconds, and the waves are 20 m apart. Calculate the velocity of the wave.

Section II Wave Phenomena

1. A county is 6,000 m wide and 60,000 m long. A radio station
    will be broadcasting at $9 \cdot 10^5$ Hz from two transmitters located
    in the middle of the county. The first nodal line will extend
    to the county line 3,000 m away. What is the wave length
    of the radio wave and the proper separation between the antennas?

2. An interference pattern is produced in a ripple tank. The
    sources are 3 cm apart. The distance from the center to the
    first nodal line is 2.5 cm. The distance from the sources
    to the first nodal line is 15 cm. What is the wave length
    of the wave?

Section III Sound Waves

1. A bat uses a type of sonar device in flying. It emits sounds
    and orients by an analysis of the reflections of those sounds.
    If a bat sends out sound at 330 $\frac{m}{sec.}$ and hears the reflection
    0.1 sec. later, how close is the object?

2. A student uses a tuning fork and a velocity of sound apparatus
    and discovers the first maximum amplitude sound at an air depth
    of 30 cm and the second at 88 cm. The room temperature is
    30°C. Calculate the velocity of the sound, wave length of the
    wave, and the frequency of the tuning fork.

ADDITIONAL ACTIVITIES, Answer Key

Section I   Energy Transfer

1. $v = f\lambda$

$f = \dfrac{v}{\lambda}$

$= \dfrac{330 \;\dfrac{m}{sec.}}{3 \; m} = 110 \; Hz$

$T = \dfrac{1}{f} = \dfrac{1}{110} \; Hz$

$= \dfrac{1}{110} \; sec. = .009 \; sec.$

$T = 2 \; sec.$

$f = \tfrac{1}{2} Hz$

2. $v = f\lambda$

$= (\tfrac{1}{2} Hz)(20 \; m)$

$= 10 \; \dfrac{m}{sec.}$

Section II   Wave Phenomena

1. $v = f\lambda$

$\lambda = \dfrac{v}{f}$

$\lambda = \dfrac{3 \cdot 10^{8} \; \dfrac{m}{sec.}}{9 \cdot 10^{5} \; Hz}$

$\lambda = 333 \; m$

$\dfrac{(n - \tfrac{1}{2})}{d} = \dfrac{X}{L}$

$\dfrac{(n - \tfrac{1}{2})(333)}{d} = \dfrac{3000 \; m}{30,000 \; m}$

$\dfrac{(\tfrac{1}{2})(333)}{d} = \dfrac{1}{10}$

$d = 1665$

2. $\dfrac{(n - \tfrac{1}{2})\lambda}{d} = \dfrac{X}{L}$

$\dfrac{(1 - \tfrac{1}{2})\lambda}{3 \; cm} = \dfrac{2.5 \; cm}{15 \; cm}$

$\dfrac{\tfrac{1}{2}\lambda}{3 \; cm} = \dfrac{2.5 \; cm}{15 \; cm}$

$\tfrac{1}{2}\lambda = \dfrac{3(2.5)}{15} \; cm$

$\lambda = \dfrac{2(3)(2.5)}{15} \; cm$

$\lambda = \dfrac{15}{15} = 1 \; cm$

Section III   Sound Waves

1. $v = \dfrac{d}{t}$ $\qquad\qquad$ $d = (330\ \dfrac{m}{sec.})(.1\ sec.)$

$\quad$ $d = vt$ $\qquad\qquad$ $d = 33$ m but this is double the path of 16.5 m

2. $v = 330 + .6\ C°\ \dfrac{m}{sec.}$

$\qquad = 330 + (.6)(30°C)$

$\qquad = 348\ \dfrac{m}{sec.}$

$\dfrac{t}{2}\lambda = L_2 - L_1$

$\qquad = 88 - 30$ cm

$\qquad = 58$ cm

$\lambda = 116$ cm

$\quad = 1.16$ m

$v = f\lambda$

$f = \dfrac{v}{\lambda}$

$\quad = \dfrac{348\ \dfrac{m}{sec.}}{1.16\ m}$

$f = 300$ Hz

MATERIALS NEEDED

Section I

Page 4   mirror, pencil, flashlight, paper, ruler, protractor,
          ball bearing

Page 6   cube of glass, protractor, pen light

Page 7   ball bearing ($\frac{1}{2}$ inch diameter or larger), paper, carbon
          paper, cardboard, incline, protractor

Page 9   semicircular plastic dish, ruler, protractor, 15 pins,
          graph paper, cardboard

Page 12   glass water tank, mirror, string, pencil light beam, cube
          of glass, light pipe

Page 14   2 Polaroid filters

Section II

Page 19   2-plane mirrors, pins, clay, ruler, protractor, cardboard,
          paper

Page 23   ripple tank, rubber hose, dowel, light source

Page 26   battery, low-powered light, meter stick, converging lens,
          clay, adding machine tape

Section III

Page 33   razor blade, lamp, red filter, blue filter, meter stick,
          stand, liquid graphite, 2 glass slides

Page 36   straight filament lamp, 2 razor blades, red filter,
          blue filter, meter stick, stand, 2 glass slides,
          liquid graphite

ADDITIONAL ACTIVITIES
    The following activities may be reproduced as student worksheets.

Section I Speed and Properties

1. What is the frequency of light with a wave length of $5 \cdot 10^{-7}$ m?

2. Could light of frequency $8 \cdot 10^{14}$ have a wave length of $4 \cdot 10^{-7}$? Explain.

3. Calculate the speed of light in water if the index of refraction is 1.33.

4. If the speed of light in glass is $2 \cdot 10^8 \frac{m}{sec.}$, calculate the index of refraction.

Section II Mirrors and Lenses

1. Draw the three principal rays and locate the image of an object placed in front of a concave mirror. Is this a real or virtual image? Is it enlarged or diminished? Erect or inverted?

2. Draw the three principal rays and locate the image of an object placed in front of a convex lens. Is this a real or virtual image? Enlarged or diminished? Erect or inverted?

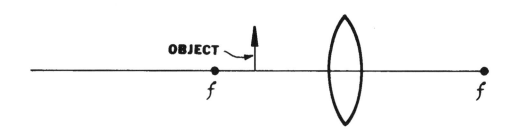

3. An object 6 cm high is placed 15 cm from the focus of a 5 cm focal length concave mirror. Calculate the image height.

4. What is the distance of the image from the focal length in Problem 3?

5. If the focal length of a convex lens is 8 cm, locate the image if the object is place 4 cm from the focal length.

6. What other information is needed to calculate the height of the image?

ADDITIONAL ACTIVITIES, Answer Key

Section I Speed and Properties

1. $c = f\lambda$

$3 \cdot 10^8 \dfrac{\text{m}}{\text{sec.}} = f(5 \cdot 10^{-7}\text{ m})$

$f = \dfrac{3 \cdot 10^8 \dfrac{\text{m}}{\text{sec.}}}{5 \cdot 10^{-7}\text{ m}} = .6 \cdot 10^{15} \qquad \dfrac{1}{\text{sec.}} = 6.0 \cdot 10^{14}\text{ Hz}$

2. $c = f\lambda$

$= (8 \cdot 10^{14}\text{ Hz})(4 \cdot 10^{-7}\text{ m})$

$c = 32 \cdot 10^7 \dfrac{\text{m}}{\text{sec.}} = 3.2 \cdot 10^8 \dfrac{\text{m}}{\text{sec.}}$

No, because the value for "c" cannot be greater than $3 \cdot 10^8 \dfrac{\text{m}}{\text{sec.}}$ which is the speed of light in a vacuum.

3. $n = \dfrac{c}{v}$

$1.33 = \dfrac{3 \cdot 10^8 \dfrac{\text{m}}{\text{sec.}}}{v}$

$v = \dfrac{3 \cdot 10^8 \dfrac{\text{m}}{\text{sec.}}}{1.33}$

$v = 2.25 \cdot 10^8 \dfrac{\text{m}}{\text{sec.}}$

4. $n = \dfrac{c}{v} = \dfrac{3 \cdot 10^8 \dfrac{\text{m}}{\text{sec.}}}{2 \cdot 10^8 \dfrac{\text{m}}{\text{sec.}}}$

$n = \dfrac{3}{2} = 1.5$

Section II Mirrors and Lenses

1.
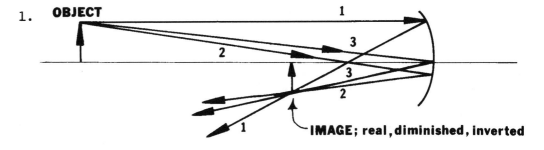

IMAGE; real, diminished, inverted

2.

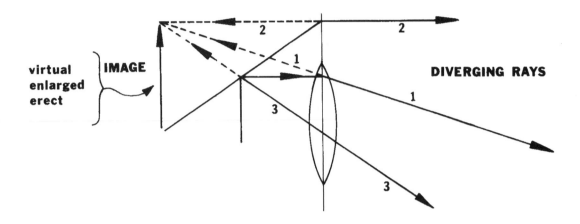

virtual enlarged erect { **IMAGE**   **DIVERGING RAYS**

3. $\dfrac{H_o}{H_i} = \dfrac{S_o}{f}$; $\dfrac{6 \text{ cm}}{H_i} = \dfrac{15 \text{ cm}}{5 \text{ cm}}$

   $15\, H_i = 30 \text{ cm}$

   $H_i = 2 \text{ cm}$

4. Either of these:

   $S_i S_o = f^2$

   $S_i = \dfrac{(5 \text{ cm})^2}{15 \text{ cm}}$

   $\quad\quad = 1\tfrac{2}{3} \text{ cm}$

   $\dfrac{H_o}{H_i} = \dfrac{f}{S_i}$; $\dfrac{6 \text{ cm}}{2 \text{ cm}} = \dfrac{5 \text{ cm}}{S_i}$

   $6\, S_i = 10 \text{ cm}$

   $S_i = 1\tfrac{2}{3} \text{ cm}$

5. $S_o S_i = f^2$

   $(4 \text{ cm})(S_i) = (8 \text{ cm})^2 = 64 \text{ cm}^2$

   $S_i = \dfrac{64 \text{ cm}^2}{4 \text{ cm}}$

   $S_i = 18 \text{ cm}$

6. $\dfrac{H_o}{H_i} = \dfrac{S_o}{f}$ or $\dfrac{H_o}{H_i} = \dfrac{f}{S_i}$; You need to know the height of the object.

MATERIALS NEEDED

Section I

glass wand, Bakelite (or hard rubber) wand, silk cloth, 2 pith balls, 2 silk threads, wool cloth (or cat's fur), stand for suspending pith balls

Section II

None

Section III

None

ADDITIONAL LEARNING ACTIVITIES

Section I   Electric Charges

1. Write a skit about Benjamin Franklin's kite experiment and his later work with electricity. Present your skit to the class.

2. Connect a $1\frac{1}{2}$-volt battery to a porcelain socket with a flashlight bulb. Disconnect one of the connections and make contact using assorted types of wires, plastics, wooden objects, and glass items. Which items conduct electricity and allow the bulb to light? Write a brief report on your findings.

3. Run a comb briskly through your hair and hold the comb close to a fine stream of water. Report your results and the reasons for them.

4. Make a poster stressing safety rules that should be observed during an electrical storm. Include the scientific reasoning behind every rule.

5. Comb your hair and then pick up small bits of paper with the comb. Repeat the action, each time touching the comb to another object before approaching the paper bits. Touch a variety of metal, wood, plastic, and glass objects. Explain the difference in action on the paper. Draw sketches of each test action showing the location and path of electrons as they leave the comb.

Section II Electric Fields

1. Place a bar magnet under a glass pan of water. Magnetize a
   sewing needle by stroking it with a magnet. Gently place the
   needle on top of the water near one end of the bar magnet.
   Watch and then sketch the path taken by the needle. Repeat
   by placing the needle in various areas and observing its motion.
   The final sketch will show the lines of force of the magnet.

Section III Electric Potential

1. Talk to an auto mechanic and ask for an explanation of an automobile capacitor. Write a brief report on what you have learned.

MATERIALS NEEDED
    None

ADDITIONAL LEARNING ACTIVITIES

    Section I Current

        1. Connect a copper wire to both terminals of a dry cell
            battery. Immediately touch the wire and keep your fingers
            on the wire until you feel the heat. What is causing the
            heat?

        2. Visit a hardware store and observe all of the types and
            sizes of batteries. Make a list of voltages represented
            and the uses for the various types of battery. Ask the
            store owner for information on other battery types that
            may be listed in the order book.

        3. Find out the principles behind hydroelectric power either
            by field trip or using an encyclopedia.

    Section II Resistance

        1. Ask an electrician or your parents to show you a fuse. New
            electrical systems have breakers instead of fuses. Find out
            why breakers are safer.

    Section III Circuits

        1. Obtain three 1.5 volt dry cells and the bulb portion of a
            flashlight. Try wiring one, then two, and then all three
            batteries, first in series, and then in parallel. Note the
            brightness of the lightbulb under all of the arrangements.
            Which gives the most light, and why?

        2. Ask an electrician or someone from the local power company
            how they determine the size of a service entrance to use on
            a new residence or business. Plan a home and then deter-
            mine the proper service entrance that should be installed
            using the information you obtain.

Science 1208 Teacher Notes

MATERIALS NEEDED

Section I

Page 5   2 bar magnets, 3 sheets of stiff cardboard, iron filings

Section II

Page 14   copper, 1 meter long; small porcelain lamp socket and bulb; wire cutter or 8-inch scissors; dry cell; compass;

Section III

None

ADDITIONAL LEARNING ACTIVIITES

Section I   Fields and Forces

1. Research the cause of the aurora borealis and write a detailed report on the phenomenon. Include sketches.

2. Read about Arctic exploration and the problems that a compass presents when it is used so near the magnetic North Pole.

3. Borrow a high-quality compass. Practice using the compass to find north, then hold it and walk toward a car, metal bridge, or any metal structure. Note the deflection of the needle.

4. Test several objects with a magnet. Make a list of items that are attracted and those that are not attracted. Write a general statement about each list.

5. Write a history of the experiments of Faraday and Henry (see page 17), indicating in detail their electromagnetic induction discoveries, with emphasis upon the type of technique used by each to explain the same phenomenon. Three double-spaced pages would be adequate.

Section II   Electromagnetism

1. Walk under a power line with a compass in hand. Note the deflection of the needle.

2. Most hospitals have emergency generators. Learn how a gas generator works to produce electricity. Make and label a large sketch showing how a generator functions.

Section III   Electron Beams

1. Edison is credited with the vacuum tube. Find out why vacuum tubes are important and list their common uses.

2. Visit an auto testing station to view their diagnostic equipment. Ask in advance if you can observe the equipment in use.

MATERIALS NEEDED

Suggested for LIFEPAC:

calculator with scientific notation
encyclopedia

ADDITIONAL LEARNING ACTIVITIES

Section I   Quantum Theory

1. Talk to an X-ray technician to learn about the precautions technicians take to avoid exposure to X rays. Ask about the potential damage that can result from overexposure to X rays.

2. Practice making rainbows after reading about them in an encyclopeida or science book. Give a brief demonstration and explanation to a younger group of students after obtaining permission.

3. Use original materials and make a model of a simple atom using the Thomson model. Construct another model of the same atom using the Rutherford concept.

Section II   Nuclear Theory

1. Talk to a medical person and learn about the isotopes used in medicine. List all of the isotopes and give at least one disease or test that makes use of that chemical.

2. Madam Curie may have suffered and died from overexposure to isotopes. Write a brief report on her final illness.

3. Write a report on Einstein's $E = MC^2$ equation and how this equation shows that the mass defect equals binding energy.

4. Obtain 100 sugar cubes and put a dot of ink on one side of each. Toss the cubes gently in a paper bag and roll out onto a pan. Record each toss number and write down the number of cubes that landed dot side up and the number of cubes that did not. Consider that each cube that landed dot side up is a molecule that has undergone radioactive decay. Remove the decayed molecules after each toss. Continue tossing the cubes until all have decayed. Use the graphs on page 30 as examples and plot both curves. Tosses will be your unit of time.

Section III Nuclear Reactions

1. Interview a civil defense officer and learn about the dangers of alpha, gamma, and beta radiation. What kind of protection is needed for each type of radiation? How can each type of material be transported and stored safely?

2. Write a scientific report on the nuclear processes that occur in the sun.

3. Draw a large map of Canada and the United States. Plot all of the nuclear power plants that you can on the map.

MATERIALS NEEDED
None

ADDITIONAL LEARNING ACTIVITIES

Section I Mechanics

None

Section II Wave Motion

None

Section III Electricity

1. Write a monologue as if Ben Franklin were telling a group about his discoveries in electricity.

2. Make a list of all the appliances or devices in a home or school that use electromagnets.

   Examples:
   door bell, chimes, water valves and cycle changers in washing machines and dishwashers, class bells, timed irrigation systems, automatic ice cube maker, electric door locks, car starter solenoid

Section IV Modern Physics

1. Write a story or play about the development of the atomic model and the people involved or write about the life of Madam Curie. Make your story or play scientifically correct but suitable for students of the upper elementary grades. Ask for permission to present your story or play to a group.

ADDITIONAL ACTIVITIES
The following activities may be reproduced as student worksheets.

Section I Mechanics

1. A cart travels east 6 meters and then north 8 meters in 20 seconds.
    a. Calculate the displacement and velocity.
    b. Calculate the acceleration if the cart then travels in a south-easterly direction at an initial speed of 2 $\frac{m}{sec.}$ and in one minute is finally moving at 17 $\frac{m}{sec.}$

2. A cart accelerates from a standing start with an acceleration equal to that of gravity at the earth's surface and travels for 5 seconds. What is its displacement and final velocity?

3. A person (50 kg) jumps off a boat with an initial acceleration of 2 $\frac{m}{sec.}$. Calculate the force he exerts on the boat and the force the boat exerts on him. Identify which of Newton's laws is used in each calculation.

4. Newton's second law equates impulse and momentum. A boy catches a baseball (0.5 kg) moving at 30 $\frac{m}{sec.}$ in such a way that his hand "rides" with the ball for 0.6 seconds.
   a. Calculate the force of impact on his hands.
   b. Calculate the force if the impact of the ball and hand was for 0.1 second.

5. The moon is approximately 240,000 miles away and takes approximately 30 days to orbit the earth. If a satellite were placed at $\frac{1}{3}$ that distance, how many days would it take to orbit the earth?

6. A motor lifts a 10-pound object 5 feet into the air in 2 seconds. Its efficiency is 20%. Calculate a. the energy expended, b. the work being done, c. the power of the motor, and d. the energy required.

71

Section II   Wave Motion

1. Draw diagrams of both transverse and longitudinal waves in a Slinky®
    and describe their basic motions.

2. If the speed of sound is approximately 330 $\frac{m}{sec.}$ and thunder is heard
    8 seconds after a lightning bolt is seen, how far away is the storm
    in meters and kilometers?

3. Light is experimentally clocked at 6 meters in 20 nanoseconds (nano =
    billionth). Calculate the speed of light.

4. Calculate the index of refraction of a substance if light travels
    $2.5 \cdot 10^8 \frac{m}{sec.}$ in that medium.

5. Use two rays to locate the image with the lens illustrated. Is the
    image real or virtual, diminished or enlarged, inverted or erect?

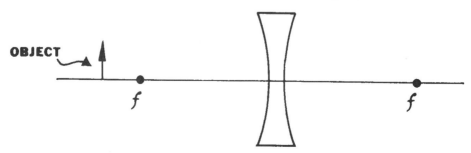

6. Use two rays to locate the image with the mirror illustrated. Is it real or virtual, diminished or enlarged, inverted or erect?

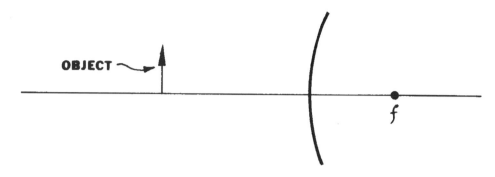

7. Use three rays to locate the image with the mirror illustrated. Is the image real or virtual, diminished or enlarged, inverted or erect?

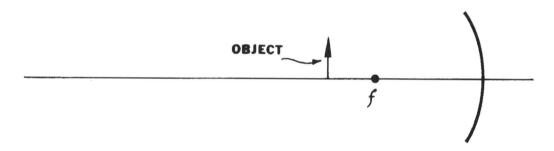

8. Use three rays to locate the image with the lens illustrated. Is it real or virtual, diminished or enlarged, inverted or erect?

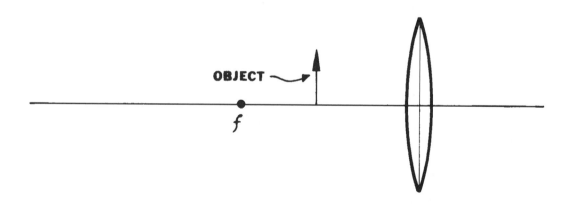

9. An object is placed in front of a lens such that a real image is formed. If the ratio of the image height to object height is 3:1 and the object is 5 cm from the focal point, what is the focal length of the lens and where is the image located?

10. What is the difference between refraction and diffraction?

11. Which phenomenon demonstrates that sound is a longitudinal wave and not a transverse wave; refraction, diffraction, interference, or polarization? Why?

12. In a ripple tank the sources are 3 cm apart and the distance to a position on the third nodal line is 30 cm from the source and 5 cm from the center line. What is the wave length of the wave?

13. In each of the phenomena listed, state whether it demonstrates the wave or the particle nature of light.

    a. refraction _____

    b. polarization _____

    c. photoelectric effect _____

    d. interference _____

    e. diffraction _____

    f. G. I. Taylor's experiment _____

Section III Electricity

    1. Calculate the current in a circuit having an emf of 15 volts and a resistance of 3 ohms.

    2. Calculate the total resistance in a circuit containing 3 resistances of $\frac{2}{3}$ ohm, $\frac{3}{4}$ ohm, and $\frac{1}{6}$ ohm in parallel.

Section IV Modern Physics

1. How many half-lives will it take for a 20 g sample of radioactive material to be reduced to 2.5 g?

2. Chlorine has two isotopes with masses of 34.969 amu and 36.966 amu. The isotope of 34.969 amu has a relative abundance of 75.53%. If chlorine were treated as a single isotope, what would be its atomic mass?

3. What are the proper symbols for a neutron, proton, deuteron, triton, and alpha particle?

ADDITIONAL ACTIVITIES, Answer Key

Section I   Mechanics

1. a.

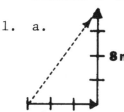

8 m

6 m

$R = 10$ m,   = displacement

$v = \dfrac{\Delta d}{\Delta t} = \dfrac{10 \text{ m}}{20 \text{ s}}$ $= 0.5 \dfrac{m}{s}$

b. $a = \dfrac{\Delta v}{\Delta t} = \dfrac{17 \frac{m}{s} - 2 \frac{m}{s}}{1 \text{ minute}} = \dfrac{15 \frac{m}{s}}{60 \text{ sec}}$

$a = 0.25 \dfrac{m}{s^2}$

2. $d = \frac{1}{2}at$

$= \frac{1}{2}(9.8 \frac{m}{s^2})(5 \text{ s})^2$

$= \frac{1}{2}(9.8)(25) \text{ m}$

$= 122.5 \text{ m}$

$v = at$

$= (9.8 \frac{m}{s^2})(5 \text{ s})$

$= 49 \dfrac{m}{s}$

3. Newton's Second Law

$F = ma$

$= (50 \text{ kg})(2 \frac{m}{s})$

$F = 100 \text{ N}$

Newton's Third Law

$F_{action} = F_{reaction}$

$F_{action} = 100 \text{ N}$

$F_{reaction} = 100 \text{ N}$

4. a. $F\Delta t = m\Delta v$

$F(0.6 \text{ s}) = (0.5 \text{ kg})(30 \frac{m}{s})$

$F = \dfrac{(0.5 \text{ kg})(30 \frac{m}{s})}{0.6 \text{ s}}$

$F = 25 \text{ N}$

b. $F\Delta t = m\Delta v$

$F(0.1 \text{ s}) = (0.5 \text{ kg})(30 \frac{m}{s})$

$F = 150 \text{ N}$

5. $\dfrac{T_m{}^2}{D_m{}^3} = \dfrac{T_s{}^2}{D_s{}^3}$

let $D_m = 1$, $T_m = 1$, $D_s = \frac{1}{3}$

$\dfrac{1^2}{1^3} = \dfrac{T_s{}^2}{(\frac{1}{3})^3}$

$T_s{}^2 = \frac{1}{27}$

$T_s = \dfrac{\sqrt{1}}{\sqrt{27}} \quad \frac{1}{5}$

T_s is approximately $\frac{1}{5}$ the time for the moon's orbit

$\frac{1}{5}$ of 30 days = 6 days

Alternate method

$\dfrac{T_m{}^2}{D_m{}^3} = \dfrac{T_s{}^2}{D_s{}^3}$

$\dfrac{(30 \text{ d})^2}{(2.4 \cdot 10^5 \text{ mi})} = \dfrac{T_s{}^2}{(.8 \cdot 10^5 \text{ mi})^3}$

$T_s{}^2 = \dfrac{(30 \text{ d})^2 (.8 \cdot 10^5 \text{ mi})^3}{(2.4 \cdot 10^5 \text{ mi})^3}$

$T_s{}^2 = (30 \text{ d})^2 (\dfrac{.8}{2.4})^3$

$= (30 \text{ d})^2 (\frac{1}{3})^3$

$= (30 \text{ d})^2 (\frac{1}{27})$

$T_s = (30 \text{ d})^2 \; \dfrac{1}{27}$

$= \dfrac{(30 \text{ d})(1)}{5} \quad$ approx

$= 6$ days approximately

6. a. $E = mgh = Fd$

   $= (10 \text{ lb})(5 \text{ ft})$

   $E = 50 \text{ ft-lb}$

   b. Work = Energy

   Work = 50 ft-lb

c. $P = \dfrac{\Delta E}{\Delta t}$

   $= \dfrac{50 \text{ ft-lb}}{2 \text{ sec}}$

   $= 25 \dfrac{\text{ft-lb}}{\text{sec}}$

d. Efficiency $= \dfrac{\text{Work out}}{\text{Work in}} \cdot 100\%$

   $20\% = \dfrac{50 \text{ ft-lb}}{\text{Work in}} \cdot 100\%$

   Work in $= 50 \text{ ft-lb} \cdot \dfrac{100}{20}$

   Work in $= 250 \text{ ft-lb}$

Section II Wave Motion

motion

motion

2. $v = \dfrac{d}{t}$; $d = vt$

   $d = (330\ \dfrac{m}{sec.})(8\ sec.)$

   $d = 2{,}640\ m$

   $d = 2.64\ km$

3. $v = \dfrac{d}{t}$

   $= \dfrac{6\ m}{20 \cdot 10^{-9}\ sec.}$

   $= \dfrac{6\ m}{2 \cdot 10^{-8}\ sec.}$

   $= 3 \cdot 10^{8}\ \dfrac{m}{sec.}$

4. $n = \dfrac{c}{v} = \dfrac{3.0 \cdot 10^{8}\ \dfrac{m}{sec.}}{v}$

   $n = \dfrac{3.0 \cdot 10^{8}\ \dfrac{m}{sec.}}{2.5 \cdot 10^{8}\ \dfrac{m}{sec.}}$

   $n = \dfrac{3.0}{2.5}$

   $n = 1.2$

5.

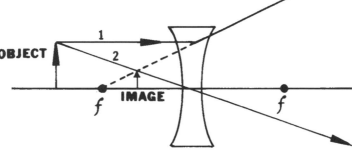

Image is virtual, diminished and erect.

6.

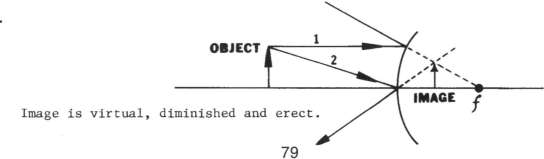

Image is virtual, diminished and erect.

7.

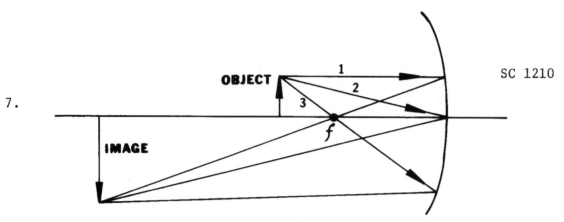

OBJECT

IMAGE

SC 1210

Image is real, inverted and enlarged.

8.

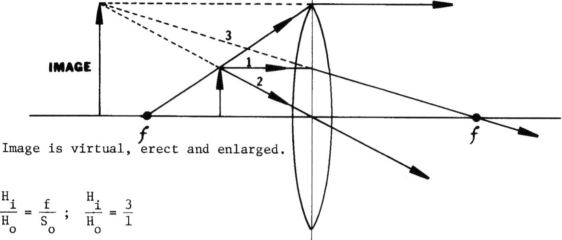

IMAGE

Image is virtual, erect and enlarged.

9. $\dfrac{H_i}{H_o} = \dfrac{f}{S_o}$; $\dfrac{H_i}{H_o} = \dfrac{3}{1}$

$\dfrac{3}{1} = \dfrac{f}{5 \text{ cm}}$

f = 15 cm

Alternate way

$S_i S_o = f$

$\dfrac{H_i}{H_o} = \dfrac{S_i}{f}$

$S_i = \dfrac{(15 \text{ cm})^2}{5 \text{ cm}}$

$\dfrac{3}{1} = \dfrac{S_i}{15 \text{ cm}}$

$S_i = 45 \text{ cm}$

$S_i = 45 \text{ cm}$

10. Refraction occurs when light travels from one medium to another. Diffraction results in the bending of light in the same medium due to the *geograph* geometrical shape of the object.

11. Only polarization because only transverse waves are affected by polarized lenses.

12. $\dfrac{x}{L} = \dfrac{(n - \frac{1}{2})\lambda}{d}$

$\dfrac{5 \text{ cm}}{30 \text{ cm}} = \dfrac{(3 - \frac{1}{2})\lambda}{3 \text{ cm}}$

$\dfrac{15 \text{ cm}}{30} = 2.5\lambda$

$\lambda = \dfrac{1}{2(2.5)} \text{ cm}$

$= \frac{1}{5} \text{ cm}$

$\lambda = 0.2 \text{ cm}$

13. a. wave
    b. wave
    c. particle
    d. wave
    e. wave
    f. particle

Section III Electricity

1. $i = \dfrac{\varepsilon}{r} = \dfrac{15 \text{ volts}}{3 \text{ ohm}} = 5 \text{ amps}$

2. $\dfrac{1}{R_T} = \dfrac{1}{R_1} + \dfrac{1}{R_2} + \dfrac{1}{R_3}$

$= \dfrac{1}{\frac{2}{3} \text{ ohm}} + \dfrac{1}{\frac{3}{4} \text{ ohm}} + \dfrac{1}{\frac{1}{6} \text{ ohm}}$

$= \frac{3}{2} \text{ ohm}^{-1} + \frac{4}{3} \text{ ohm}^{-1} + 6 \text{ ohm}^{-1}$

$= (\frac{9}{6} + \frac{8}{6} + \frac{36}{6}) \text{ ohm}^{-1}$

$= \frac{53}{6} \text{ ohm}^{-1} = \frac{6}{53} \text{ ohm}$

Section IV Modern Physics

1. $\dfrac{2.5}{20} = \dfrac{1}{8} = \dfrac{1}{2}^3 = 3$ half lives

2. $(34.969)(.7553) = 26.412$

$(36.966)(.2447) = \dfrac{9.046}{35.458} \text{ amu}$

3. neutron $_0n^1$

   proton $_1H^1$

   deuteron $_1H^2$

   triton $_1H^3$

   alpha particle $_2He^4$

81

TESTS

Reproducible Tests
for use with the Science 1200
Teacher's Guide

Name _____

Match these items (each answer, 2 points).

1. _____ The fundamental unit on this list that is synonymous with mass

2. _____ As a car slows down it undergoes ___.

3. _____ The term that describes 400 miles by road between two cities.

4. _____ Traveling in one direction (north), the car's rate of distance changes as the time fluctuates. The average calculated is ___ .

5. _____ Distance is what kind of quantity?

6. _____ A plane travels 300 mph east; what term best describes this derived quantity?

a. inertia

b. distance

c. displacement

d. scalar

e. acceleration

f. average velocity

g. velocity

Complete these calculations (each answer, 5 points).

7. A car travels from City A eastward to City B. It takes 8 hours, and the road is 400 miles long, although it is only 320 miles between cities in a straight line. What is the average speed of the car?

_____

8. A car traveling at 40 $\frac{m}{sec.}$ speeds up to 60 $\frac{m}{sec.}$ in 4 sec. What is the car's acceleration?

_____

9. A certain molecule has the volume of $16 \cdot 10^{-21}$ cm^3. If you have a known volume, you can divide the known volume by the volume of a molecule to calculate the number of molecules in that known volume. You are given a 2 mm x 2 mm x 2 mm cubic volume of the substance.

   a. What are the dimensions of the volume in centimeters?

                                            _____

   b. What is the volume of the substance ($V = lwh$) in cm^3?

                                            _____

   c. What is the volume of the substance in cm^3 using scientific notation?

                                            _____

   d. What is the number of molecules in this volume? Express the answer in scientific notation.

                                            _____

10. If the mass of a substance occupying a 3 cm x 3 cm x 3 cm cubic volume ($V = lwh$) is 81 g, what is its density?

                                            _____

11. Ike travels 2 miles east, 4 miles north, 2 miles west, and finally 4 miles south. What is his total displacement?

                                            _____

12. A model plane heads north at 8 $\frac{m}{sec.}$ in a wind east at 6 $\frac{m}{sec.}$. It is blown off course. What is its velocity along its new course? (Hint: use vectors)

_____

Answer these questions (each answer, 5 points).

13. Near the surface of the earth, the temperature decreases at high altitudes. Also, temperatures differ over land or water surfaces and change from night to day. Explain how you can describe the earth's atmosphere in terms of a temperature field. What are the difficulties involved?

_____
_____
_____
_____
_____
_____

14. What are the advantages and disadvantages of using a globe in describing the earth to an elementary school child?

_____
_____
_____
_____
_____

54 / 67

Date _____

Score _____

Name _____

Match these items (each answer, 2 points).

1. _____ $9.8 \frac{m}{sec.^2}$ is ___.

2. _____ the law that explains why an object in motion stays in motion if no forces are acting on it

3. _____ the law that explains why a boat moves backward when you dive off the front

4. _____ the law that states that $\frac{R^3}{T^2}$ is a constant for an orbiting system

5. _____ The weight mg is a(n) ___.

6. _____ what is measured by $\frac{F}{a}$ when F is the force exerted on an object and a is the acceleration it undergoes

a. Newton's First Law of Motion

b. Newton's Third Law of Motion

c. Kepler's Second Law of Motion

d. Kepler's Third Law of Motion

e. acceleration due to gravity

f. force

g. inertial mass

Complete these calculations (each answer, 5 points).

7. An object has a component of velocity $12 \frac{m}{sec.}$ to the right and $5 \frac{m}{sec.}$ down. What is the net velocity acting on the object? Use a ruler.

_____

8. A rock of 2 kg is swung in a circle with a radius of 10 m so that it makes a revolution every 2 seconds. What is the centripetal acceleration?

_____

9. If a planet at 4 AU from the sun takes "8 years" to make one revolution, then how far away from the sun is a planet that takes "1 year" to make one revolution?

    _____

10. An object is thrown down with an intial velocity of 15 $\frac{ft.}{sec.}$. How far does it fall in 2 seconds?

    _____

11. An object of mass 3 kg is accelerated to 15 $\frac{m}{sec.^2}$ by a force. If the mass were changed to 1 kg and the same force exerted, what would the acceleration be?

    _____

12. If an object (5-kg mass) initially moving to the right at 6 $\frac{m}{sec.}$ were to break into two pieces such that one piece (2 kg) moved to the right at 3 $\frac{m}{sec.}$, at what speed and in what direction is the second piece (3 kg) traveling?

    _____

Answer these questions (each answer, 5 points).

13. Why does a car spin out of control when trying to make a turn on ice?

    _____

    _____

    _____

14. Since the sun has a radius much larger than that of the earth, why would it exert a larger gravitational force on its surface?

_____

_____

_____

15. Which would exert a greater gravitational force, Planet A or Planet B, of the same diameter but smaller mass?   Why?

_____

_____

_____

46
57

Date _____

Score _____

Name _____

Match these items (each answer, 2 points).

1. _____ another term for work

2. _____ energy of a pendulum at the bottom of its swing

3. _____ energy of a compressed rubber ball

4. _____ energy contained in a tornado

5. _____ law that states that in any energy transformation, some energy is lost in the form of heat

6. _____ form of matter found in the sun

7. _____ form of matter found in air

8. _____ form of matter found in a diamond

9. _____ measures motion of molecules

10. _____ energy measured in kilocalories

a. energy

b. potential energy

c. kinetic energy

d. heat energy

e. chemical energy

f. wind energy

g. Second Law of Heat and Thermodynamics

h. solid state

i. gaseous state

j. plasma state

k. temperature

Complete these calculations (each answer, 5 points).

11. Calculate the energy of a falling rock (4 kg) that is 25 m high falling at $5 \frac{m}{sec.}$.

_____

12. Calculate the power of a motor that can lift a 5 kg object 100 meters in 5 sec.

_____

13. A steel ball of mass 2 slugs is rolling at 8 $\frac{\text{ft.}}{\text{sec.}}$. If no energy is lost due to friction, how high up an inclined plane would the ball roll. (Hint: Use the value of "g" in the English system.)

_____

14. A fulcrum system lifts a 200 lbs. weight two inches with a 20 lbs. effort. If the effort force is moved 30 inches what is the efficiency of the system?

_____

15. Given the following information on alcohol (sp. ht. = 0.6, boiling point = 78°C, latent heat of vaporization = 204 kcal/kg), what heat is needed to raise the temperature of 2 kg of alcohol from a liquid at 28°C to a vapor.

_____

16. A ball of mass $\frac{1}{2}$ slug is rolling up an incline at $8 \frac{ft.}{sec.}$. When it is 2 ft. high, if the initial energy is $100 \frac{ft.}{lb.}$ how much energy is lost in the form of heat?

_____

Date _____

Score _____

Name _____

Match these items (each answer, 2 points).

1. _____ wave of rhythmic repe-
titive oscillations

2. _____ change in frequency or
wave length of waves
when the source is
moving relative to the
observer

3. _____ type of wave that produces motion in the medium
that is perpendicular to
the wave

4. _____ superimposition of waves
producing regions of re-
inforcement and cancel-
lation

5. _____ produced when a wave
reaches a barrier and
continues

a. periodic wave

b. transverse

c. longitudinal

d. transmission

e. interference

f. doppler effect

Complete these activities (each answer, 5 points).

6. Draw a representation of the waves produced by a slowly moving wave
source.

7. Draw a representation of waves passing through a narrow opening.

8. Calculate the frequency of a light wave of wave length $6 \cdot 10^{-7}$ m.
Remember that light travels at $3 \cdot 10^8 \frac{m}{sec.}$.

9. If the speed of sound at 0°C is 330 $\frac{m}{sec.}$, what is the speed of sound at 10°C?

10. An interference pattern is projected under a ripple tank. The sources are 3 cm apart, and a point on the second nodal line is 9 cm from the center and 18 cm from the sources. What is the wave length of the wave?

11. A 510 Hz tuning fork and an unknown are struck and produce 5 beats. The unknown and a 505 Hz fork are struck and produce 10 beats. What is the frequency of the unknown tuning fork?

12. Describe the phenomenon of total internal reflection.

13. Describe the difference between diffraction and refraction of water waves.

14. Describe how a marching band could cause a bridge to vibrate.

Date _____

Score _____

Science 1205 Alternate Test

Name _____

Match these items (each answer, 2 points).

1. _____ reason for blue skies
at noon and for red sun-
rises and sunsets

2. _____ a pencil appears bent
when inserted in a glass
of water

3. _____ principle that mirrors
work on

4. _____ man first credited with
trying to measure the
speed of light

5. _____ $3 \cdot 10^8 \frac{m}{sec.}$

6. _____ experiment that proved
diffraction could be a
particle phenomenon

a. Galileo

b. Michaelson

c. formula for speed of light

d. reflection

e. refraction

f. scattering

g. Taylor's experiment

Complete these activities (each answer, 5 points).

7. Using three principal rays, locate the image of an object placed in front
of the lens shown below. Identify whether the image is real or virtual,
enlarged or diminished, erect or inverted.

_____

_____

object

8. A diffraction pattern is formed when light passes through one slit. The light source is 1 meter away, the wave length of light is $6 \cdot 10^{-7}$ m, and the distance from the center to the first nodal line (dark band) is 2 mm. What is the width of the slit?

_____

9. An object 8 cm tall is placed in front of a converging mirror 24 cm from the focal point. If the image appears 6 cm from the focal point, calculate the focal length of the mirror and the height of the image.

_____

10. The speed of light in air is $3 \cdot 10^8 \frac{m}{sec.}$ but in a particular medium it is $1.5 \cdot 10^8 \frac{m}{sec.}$. Determine the index of refraction for this medium.

_____

11. The index of refraction for water is 1.33. In the picture below, draw what happens to a ray of light as it passes from air to water.

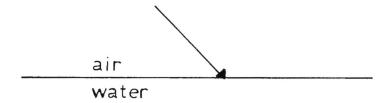

12. Discuss two basic differences between diffraction and interference, and which experiment was used to first demonstrate the particle nature of light.

_____

_____

_____

_____

_____

_____

13. Discuss one investigation that did not support the particle nature of light and one that did demonstrate that light at times behaves as a particle.

_____

_____

_____

_____

_____

_____

38 / 47

Date _____

Score _____

Name _____

Write the letter for the correct answer on each line (each answer, 2 points).

1. Positive charges may be formed by using a _____ rod.

   a. rubbed glass   c. zinc
   b. rubbed bakelite   d. carbon

2. Negative charges are attracted by _____.

   a. negative bodies   c. neutral bodies
   b. positive bodies   d. outer space

3. Electrical charges do not exist in _____.

   a. the atmosphere   c. the sea
   b. outer space   d. a, b, and c

4. An insulator _____.

   a. conducts electrons
   b. resists conduction of electrons
   c. repels positive charges
   d. is neutral

5. Coulomb's Law predicts that _____.

   a. like charges attract c. unlike charges repel
   b. like charges repel   d. none of these

6. An electrical field has _____.

   a. direction but not magnitude c. magnitude and direction
   b. magnitude but not direction d. none of these

7. A potential may be found from its _____.

   a. electrical field   c. separation
   b. distance   d. conductivity

8. Electric fields exist in _____.

   a. the sea   c. both a and b
   b. a battery   d. animals

9. A steady flow of electrical charge is called _____.

   a. a potential   c. an electrical current
   b. a potential energy source d. a field

10. A battery contains _____.

    a. negative charges   c. no charge
    b. positive charges   d. negative and positive charges

Complete these statements (each answer, 5 points).

11. The energy stored on the plates of a capacitor is found from the formula W = a._____. If the potential across the plates is doubled, the energy stored is increased b._____ times. The capacitance C of a capacitor is given by the formula c._____. A large value of C indicates a large storage of d._____ per unit of voltage applied to its plates.

12. A battery is a more useful source of current than a capacitor, since it can provide a a._____ source of b._____.

40	
	50

Date _____

Score _____

Name _____

Write *true* or *false* (each answer, 1 point).

1. _____ Only two basic kinds of electrical charge exist.

2. _____ Coulomb's Law relates voltage to current and resistance.

3. _____ According to Coulomb's Law, like charges attract.

4. _____ Capacitance is the charge stored per volt.

5. _____ Electrical current flow is similar to the flow of water in a channel.

6. _____ In a series circuit total resistance is the sum of individual resistances.

7. _____ The same current flows in every part of a series circuit.

8. _____ Ohm's Law relates voltage to resistance and power.

9. _____ Watt's Law relates voltage and current to power.

10. _____ Electrons flow out of the negative battery terminal into the positive terminal.

Complete these activities (each answer, 5 points).

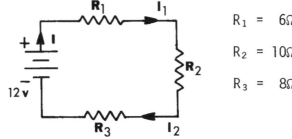

$R_1 = 6\Omega$

$R_2 = 10\Omega$

$R_3 = 8\Omega$

Find: The battery current I_b, the total resistance R_T, and the power in each resistor.

11. I_b = _____ amperes

12. R_{Total} = _____ ohms

13. Power in R_1 = _____ watts

14. Power in R_2 = _____ watts

15. Power in R_3 = _____ watts

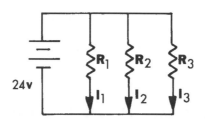

R_1 = 8Ω

R_2 = 12Ω

R_3 = 24Ω

Find: The current in each resistor and the total resistance R_T.   How
much power is delivered by the battery?

16. I_1 = _____ amperes

17. I_2 = _____ amperes

18. I_3 = _____ ampere(s)

19. R_{Total} = _____ ohms

20.   Power delivered by battery = _____ watts

Date _____

Score _____

Name _____

Answer *true* or *false* (each answer, 1 point).

1. _____ Magnetic fields exist under power lines.

2. _____ Magnetic poles always occur in pairs.

3. _____ The north pole of a magnet is a south-seeking pole.

4. _____ The aurora borealis is formed by currents from outer space.

5. _____ A force exists on every electrical charge moving in a magnetic field.

6. _____ A force exists on an electrical charge moving along a magnetic field line.

7. _____ The magnetic force law is similar to Coulomb's Law.

8. _____ The force between two magnetic poles varies inversely as the separation between the poles.

9. _____ A time varying magnetic field is always accompanied by a time varying electric field.

10. _____ A current produces a magnetic field.

Complete these statements (each answer, 3 points).

11. A magnetic field will produce a current if the field is moving relative to the _____.

12. In Faraday's experiments, current flowed only when a magnet was _____.

13. Henry's experiment produced a changing magnetic field and a current in the secondary loop using a time varying _____.

14. A potential, not a true force, is called _____.

15. Henry's induction experiments involved a simple _____.

16. The right-hand rule will give the direction of the _____ produced by a current moving normal to a magnetic field.

17. The field around a solenoid is similar to that of a _____.

18. A field around a current-carrying coil is called a _____ field.

19. Electron current flows _____ to that of conventional current.

20. The field around a magnet is a _____ field.

21. J. J. Thomson discovered the _____ in 1897.

22. In Thomson's experiment the electron beam was deflected by both

    a._____ and b._____ fields.

23. A diagnostic instrument in materials testing, automobile repair, and

    electronics is the _____ ray tube.

24. Voltage on the control grid of a CRT will control the _____
    of the spot on the screen.

25. By his beam experiments, J. J. Thomson found the ratio of a._____

    to b._____ of an electron.

49 / 61

Date _____

Score _____

Name _____

Answer *true* or *false* (each answer, 1 point).

1. _____ The atomic number is the sum of protons plus neutrons.

2. _____ Fission is the combining of two nuclei.

3. _____ A beta particle is an electron.

4. _____ A fission reaction can release 200 Mev of energy.

5. _____ Hot materials emit electromagnetic radiation.

6. _____ Binding energy holds the nucleus together.

7. _____ Mev is a unit of energy.

8. _____ Radioactive decay removes excess energy from a nucleus.

9. _____ Nuclear forces are stronger than gravity.

10. _____ Radiation is used for medical purposes.

Write the letter for the correct answer on each line (each answer, 2 points).

11. A radioactive material has a half life of 20 minutes. After two hours what fraction of the material remains? _____

    a. $\frac{1}{4}$ c. $\frac{1}{16}$
    b. $\frac{1}{64}$ d. $\frac{1}{256}$

12. The number of nucleons in a nucleus is equal to _____.

    a. the atomic number
    b. the atomic number plus the mass number
    c. the mass number
    d. none of these

13. To produce a photoelectron, the light must have large enough _____.

    a. intensity   c. wave length
    b. frequency   d. mass

14. Alpha decay will cause a nucleus to reduce by 2 its _____.

    a. mass number   c. mass
    b. atomic number   d. nucleon number

15. The binding energy curve shows that the greatest binding energy per nucleon occurs around mass number _____.

    a. 2   c. 20
    b. 8   d. 100

Complete these statements (each answer, 3 points).

16. In fusion two light nuclei join to form a heavier one and liberate

    _____.

17. Photons are also known as _____.

18. The uncertainty principle states that the product of uncertainties in

    the a._____ and b._____ of a particle is

    approximately equal to Planck's Constant.

19. To explain X-ray emission you must use _____ theory.

20. The fission chain reaction in uranium produces fission fragments, energy,

    and _____.

21. A hot gas emits a a._____ spectrum and a heated

    solid produces a b._____ spectrum.

22. De Broglie proposed that the wave length of a particle be defined as

    Planck's Constant divided by the particle's _____.

23. Bohr's model binds the electron to the nucleus with _____

    force.

Complete these calculations (each answer, 5 points).

24. Calculate the wave length of an electron traveling at $10^5 \frac{M}{sec.}$.

    _____

25. Calculate the maximum energy photoelectron that can be ejected from a
    surface requiring a 2 ev, by a photon with $\lambda = 10^{-7}$ M?

    _____

106

Name _____

Match these items (each answer, 2 points).

1. _____ magnetic field

2. _____ uncertainty principle

3. _____ potential energy

4. _____ $n = \dfrac{c}{v}$

5. _____ half life

6. _____ kinematics

7. _____ binding energy

8. _____ Dalton

9. _____ atom

10. _____ alpha particle

a. atomic scientist

b. time for 50 per cent of reduc-
   tion in radioactivity

c. study of motion

d. holds nucleus together

e. from Greek for *indivisible*

f. small particles are altered by
   measuring

g. index of refraction

h. helium nuclei

i. energy of position

j. transverse wave

k. created by moving electrical
   charges

Write the letter for the correct answer on each line (each answer, 2 points

11. The product of mass and velocity is _____.

    a. displacement   c. velocity
    b. impulse   d. momentum

12. The study of force and its effect on objects is _____.

    a. gravity   c. Kepler's Law
    b. dynamics   d. conservation

13. A wave that oscillates perpendicularly to the direction of wave travel
    is a _____.

    a. transverse wave   c. rarefaction
    b. longitudinal wave   d. condensation

14. Kepler determined that planets moved in _____.

    a. circles   c. equal times
    b. elliptical orbits   d. equal areas

15. Light has the characteristics of a _____.

    a. wave   c. wave and a particle
    b. particle   d. smooth bell curve

16. A sphere of influence is a _____.

    a. wave
    b. field
    c. vector
    d. test charge

17. Resistance in a conductor is directly proportional to _____.

    a. width
    b. length
    c. mass
    d. diameter

18. Most of the mass of an atom is in the _____.

    a. subshells
    b. electrons
    c. orbitals
    d. nucleus

19. An absorption spectrum has a series of _____.

    a. dark lines
    b. bright lines
    c. invisible lines
    d. frequency lines

20. The basic laws of motion were developed by _____.

    a. Einstein
    b. Newton
    c. Bohr
    d. Rutherford

Match these items (each answer, 2 points).

21. _____ diffraction
22. _____ velocity
23. _____ protons
24. _____ Rutherford
25. _____ force
26. _____ impulse
27. _____ mm
28. _____ gravity
29. _____ reflection
30. _____ energy

a. nucleus with orbiting electrons
b. a force acting during a time interval
c. millimeter
d. push or pull
e. ability to do work
f. equals atomic number
g. bending of light
h. bouncing off a boundary
i. rate of displacement per time
j. electron
k. attraction of earth for an object

Complete the following calculations (each answer, 5 points).

31. Calculate the frequency of a light source whose wave length is $4 \cdot 10^{-7}$.

32. Calculate the refractive index of a medium whose light slows down to $2.0 \cdot 10^{8} \, \frac{m}{sec.}$.

33. Use three rays and sketch the image.

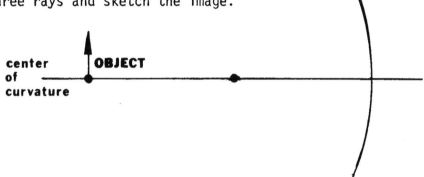

34. Calculate the height of the image in Problem 33 if the object is 3 cm high.

Date _____

Score _____

Data Tables can be found throughout the curriculum. They should be available to the student (where appropriate) anytime they are answering problems in section exercises, Self Tests, or LIFEPAC Tests.

1.1   time

1.2   length

1.3   mass or inertia

1.4   kinematics

1.5   varies, depending on grade of paper used. Approximately 400 g.

1.6   varies, depending on grade of paper used. Approximately 4 g.

1.7   varies, depending on size of paper used. Approximately 600

1.8   varies, depending on size of paper used. Approximately 0.007 g.

1.9   varies, depending on the sensitivity of the balance.

1.10   varies, depending on the size of paper used. Approximately 0.007 g. or less.

1.11   Unless the hair is dyed, black hair strands are more massive.

1.12 4×10^{-6}

1.13 4.8×10^{-3}

1.14 3×10^{4}

1.15   4.560 km.

1.16 7.3×10^{-3} g

1.17   50 μs

1.18   a. c
        b. 6.2 m north is not a scalar since it not only designates a magnitude (6.2 m) but also specifies a direction.

1.19

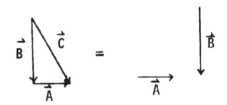

1.20

1.21

1.22

II. SECTION TWO

2.1   Yes, then draws together.

2.2   5%

2.3   10% of 5%, or 0.5%

2.4 $\frac{1}{50}$ cm³ = .02 cm³

2.5   5% of .02 cm³ = (.005)(.02) = 1 x 10^{-4} cm³

2.6   varies: approximately 15 cm

2.7   varies: approximately 900 cm^2

2.8   varies from 8×10^{-8} cm to
       7×10^{-7} cm

2.9   varies: approximately 1×10^{-21}
       cm^3

2.10   varies: approximately $\dfrac{1 \times 10^{-4}}{1 \times 10^{-21}}$

       which equals 1×10^{17} molecules

2.11   varies: approximately (0.89 gm/cm^3)
       (1×10^{-21} cm^3) which equals 0.89×10^{-21} or 8.9×10^{-22} g

2.12   298 cm, assuming that on the 99th
       try he reaches the top but can not
       pull himself over before sliding
       1 cm down. On the 100th try he
       simply goes 1 cm to get to the top
       of the wall. (99 trys x 3 cm) +
       1 cm = 298 cm

2.13   100 cm (or 1 m) up

2.14   298 cm + 100 cm = 398 cm

2.15   0 cm

2.16

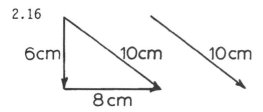

6cm   10cm   10cm
       8cm

III. SECTION THREE

3.1   adult check

3.2   300 cm

3.3   600 s

3.4   .5 cm/s
       $s = \dfrac{\Delta d}{\Delta t}$
       $= \dfrac{300 \text{ cm}}{600 \text{ s}} = .5$ cm/s

3.5   70 km

3.6   1 hr

3.7   s avg. = $\dfrac{\text{total distance}}{\text{total time}}$
              = $\dfrac{70 \text{ km}}{1 \text{ hr}}$ 70 km PH

3.8   s avg. = $\dfrac{\text{total distance}}{\text{total time}}$
              = $\dfrac{70 \text{ km}}{1 \text{ hr}}$ 70 km PH

3.9   5   5

       6   6

       9   9

       7   7

       3   3

3.10   no they vary; as hand moved forward
       dots were farther apart.

3.11   No, because the hand swung back
       and forth.

3.12   varies, would be larger speed
       values.

3.13   Because the dots are further apart
       indicating high speeds.

3.14   varies, would be smaller speed
       values.

3.15   Because hand moving back indicates
       less distance covered forward.

3.16   varies

3.17   Yes, it could be larger than
       some and smaller than others.

3.18   adult check

3.19   300 up
       +100 down
       400 cm   (rounded)

114

3.20 $s \text{ avg} = \dfrac{\text{total distance}}{\text{total time}}$

$= \dfrac{400 \text{ cm}}{600 \text{ s}}$

$= 2/3 \text{ cm/s}$

3.21 $v = \dfrac{\Delta d}{\Delta t} = \dfrac{100 \text{ cm}\uparrow}{600 \text{ s}}$

$= \dfrac{1}{6} \text{ cm/s} \uparrow$

$= \dfrac{1}{6} \text{ cm/s up}$

3.22 $\vec{v} = \dfrac{\Delta d}{\Delta t}$ but $\Delta d = 0$ cm

$\vec{v} = \dfrac{0 \text{ cm}}{600 \text{ s}} = 0 \text{ cm/s}$

3.23 $s = \dfrac{\Delta d}{\Delta t}$

$= \dfrac{40 \text{ mi}}{1 \text{ hr}}$

$= 40 \text{ mph}$

3.24 $\vec{v} = \dfrac{\Delta d}{\Delta t}$

$= \dfrac{40 \text{ mi, north}}{1 \text{ hr}}$

$= 40 \text{ mph, north}$

3.25 $s \text{ avg} = \dfrac{\text{total distance}}{\text{total time}}$

$= \dfrac{200 \text{ miles}}{5.5 \text{ hr}}$

$= 36.4 \text{ mph}$

3.26 $\vec{v} \text{ avg} = \dfrac{\Delta d}{\Delta t}$

$= \dfrac{0}{\Delta t} \leftarrow$ round trip

$\vec{v} \text{ avg} = 0$

3.27 $s = \dfrac{\Delta d}{\Delta t} = \dfrac{400 \text{ mi}}{8 \text{ hr}}$

$s = 50 \text{ mph}$

3.28 $\vec{v} = \dfrac{\Delta d}{\Delta t} = \dfrac{320 \text{ miles, north}}{8 \text{ hr}}$

$v = 40 \text{ mph, north}$

IV. SECTION FOUR

4.1 $a = \dfrac{\Delta v}{\Delta t}$

$= \dfrac{60 \text{ ft/s} - 45 \text{ ft/s east}}{5 \text{ s}}$

$= \dfrac{15 \text{ ft/s}}{5 \text{ s}} = 3 \text{ ft/s}^2, \text{ east}$

4.2 $\vec{a} = \dfrac{\Delta \vec{v}}{\Delta t} = \dfrac{30 \text{ mph} - 60 \text{ mph}}{12 \text{ min}}$

$= \dfrac{30 \text{ mph} - 60 \text{ mph, south}}{1/5 \text{ hr}}$

$= \dfrac{-30 \text{ mph, south}}{1/5 \text{ hr}}$

$= -150 \text{ mi/hr}^2, \text{ south}$

4.3

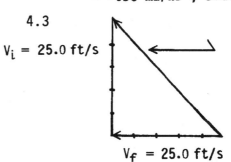

$V_i = 25.0 \text{ ft/s}$

$V_f = 25.0 \text{ ft/s}$

$V_f - V_i = \Delta \vec{v} = 35.4 \text{ ft/s}$

$\vec{a} = \dfrac{\Delta \vec{v}}{\Delta t} = \dfrac{35.4 \text{ ft/s}}{0.100 \text{ s}}$ $\vec{a} = 354. \text{ ft/s}^2 \nwarrow$

$= 354. \text{ ft/s}^2$

4.4 $\vec{a} = \dfrac{v^2/R}{} = \dfrac{(20 \text{ ft/s})^2}{25 \text{ ft}}$

$= \dfrac{400 \text{ ft}^2/\text{s}^2}{25 \text{ ft}}$

4.5 adult check

4.6 adult check

4.7 adult check

4.8 $d = d_0 + v_0 t + \frac{1}{2} a t^2$

$d = 0 + 0 + \frac{1}{2}(-980 \text{ cm/s}^2)(10\text{s})^2$

$d = -49{,}000 \text{ cm or } -490 \text{ m}$

"-" indicates down

4.9 $v^2 = v_0^2 + 2a(d - d_0)$, at the top

$0 = (20 \text{ m/s})^2 + 2(-9.8 \text{ m/s}^2)d$

$\dfrac{-400 \text{ m}^2/\text{s}^2}{-19.6 \text{ m/s}^2} = d$

$\dfrac{-400 \text{ m}^2/\text{s}^2}{-19.6 \text{ m/s}^2} = +20.4 \text{ m} = d$

$d = 20.4 \text{ m}$

4.10 $d = d_0 + \frac{1}{2}(v_0 + v)t$

$d = \frac{1}{2}(20 \text{ m/s})t$

$\dfrac{20.4 \text{ m}}{10 \text{ m/s}} = t$

$t = 2.04$ s

4.11   adult check

4.12   adult check

4.13   varies, should be approximately 980 cm/s^2

4.14   The student should compare his answer to 980 cm/s^2. (His answer will probably be lower because of friction of the tape with the timer.)

V. SECTION FIVE

5.1   Isotherms cannot cross because to cross would indicate two different temperature readings for the same point.

5.2   Example:
Heat (or cold air) from the vents and heat (or cold) from outside windows and doors. It depends on the season of the year.

5.3   Varies depending on the time of the year and what type of heating/cooling system you have.

5.4   Yes. No, thermometers are an appropriate test object for temperature fields but different test objects are needed for measuring different fields.

5.5   A temperature field is a region of space which at every point a thermometer (testing object) will have a specific reading.

5.6   You would need to use a pressure gauge and get a particular reading at every point in a given region.

5.7

--	110.0
0.4	0.4
0.7	1.0
1.0	1.0
1.5	0.5
5.2	11.2
9.5	9.5
19.2	3.7
30.1	3.5
39.5	1.7

5.8   No, it shows average distance away.

5.9   A large sheet of paper twice as long and just as wide with the sun at the center and planets around and a huge field to lay the sheet of paper out.

5.10   Either use 1 meter = 1.5×10^8/km for all scales or 1/millimeter = 6400/km for all scale measurements.

5.11   110 mm or 11.0 cm or 0.110 m

5.12   No, they go at different speeds. Mercury orbits the fastest and Pluto the slowest. They are also in different planes.

5.13   No, they orbit at various angles to the sun with Pluto tilting the most away from the flat plane.

5.14   Where the sun is with respect to the galaxy, the satellites of the planets (moons), comets and so forth. Neither have we described how moons and planets affect each other.

5.15   No, they are mental constructs which may take on physical dimensions.

5.16   The model of an atom tries to convey the region where the particle might be located, its interaction with other parts, its occupation of space or volume, its electrical charge and nuclear forces along with electrical forces and also its chemical activity.

1.1   adult check

1.2   a.   15 cm

b. $\dfrac{20cm}{5cm}$ = 4 units rise
(4 units rise)(2cm/unit rise)
= 8 cm

c. $\dfrac{20cm}{0.5cm}$ = 40 units rise
(40 units rise)(2cm/unit rise)
= 80 cm

d. $\dfrac{20cm}{0.01cm}$ = 2,000 units rise
(2,000 units rise)(2cm/unit rise)
= 4,000 cm

e. an indefinite distance

1.3 $15 \dfrac{m}{sec}$

1.4   A force (friction) acts on the car to cause it to accelerate negatively (decelerate).

1.5 $F = ma; \ a = \dfrac{F}{m}$

$a = \dfrac{8\ N}{2\ kg}$

$a = 4 \dfrac{N}{kg} = 4 \dfrac{m}{sec^2}$

1.6 $a = \dfrac{F}{m}$

$= \dfrac{8\ N}{4\ kg}$

$a = 2 \dfrac{m}{s^2}$

1.7 $F\Delta t = m\Delta v; \ \Delta v = \dfrac{F\Delta t}{m}$

$v - v_0 = \dfrac{16\ N\cdot s}{2\ kg}; \ v_0 = 0$

$v = 8 \dfrac{m}{s} \left[\dfrac{N\cdot s}{kg} = \dfrac{m}{s}\right]$

1.8 $v - v_0 = 16 \dfrac{N\cdot s}{2\ kg} = 8 \dfrac{m}{s}$

$v - 3 \dfrac{m}{s} = 8 \dfrac{m}{s}$

$v = 11 \dfrac{m}{s}$

1.9 $F\Delta t = mv; \ \Delta t = \dfrac{mv}{F}$

$\Delta t = \dfrac{(50\ kg)(8 \frac{m}{s})}{200\ N}$

$\Delta t = 2s$

1.10   Yes, there may be a slight frictional force.

1.11   It probably is more uniform at slower speeds.

1.12   a straight line with a positive slope

1.13   a straight line that is parallel to the time axis

1.14a. Example: adult check

b.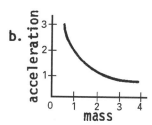

c.   a curve which shows that as mass increases, acceleration decreases; hyperbola shape

1.15a.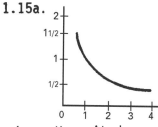

b.   Yes, it does.

1.16a. Example: adult check

force (# of bands)

   b. a straight line with a positive slope

1.17 Should be twice as much as for 3 F.

1.18 It would become infinitely large.

1.19 Place the brick on the cart and accelerate it using rubber bands; $\frac{F}{a} = m$ and $m = m_{cart} + m_{brick}$ so $m_{brick} = m - m_{cart}$.

II. SECTION TWO

2.1 $F = mg$
$= (50 \text{ kg})(9.8 \frac{m}{s^2})$
$= 490 \text{ N}$

2.2 $F = mg$
$= 50 \text{ kg}(9.8 \frac{m}{s^2})$
$= 490 \text{ N}$

2.3 $a_g = \frac{1}{5^2} g$
$= \frac{1}{25} g = .39 \frac{m}{s^2}$

$F = ma_g$
$= (50 \text{ kg})(.39 \frac{m}{s^2})$
$= 19.6 \text{ N}$

or $F = \frac{1}{25} mg$
$= \frac{1}{25} (490 \text{ N})$
$= 19.6 \text{ N}$

2.4 $F_{moon} = \frac{1}{6} F_{earth}$
$= \frac{1}{6} (490 \text{ N})$
$= 81.7 \text{ N}$

2.5 $F = mg$
$= (3 \text{ slugs})(32 \frac{ft}{s^2})$
$= 96 \text{ lb}$

2.6 $F = ma_g$; $a_g = \frac{F}{m}$

$a_g = \frac{15 \text{ lb}}{3 \text{ slugs}}$

$a_g = 5 \text{ ft/sec}^2$

2.7 The mass of a person does not change regardless of where he is. His weight depends on the acceleration due to gravity at his location, because weight = ma_g.

2.8 $d = -\frac{1}{2} gt^2$
$= -\frac{1}{2} (9.8 \frac{m}{s^2})(3 \text{ s})^2$

$d = -44 \text{ m}$
Object fell 44 m; therefore, the building is 44 m tall (the minus sign means <u>downward</u>).

2.9 $v = -gt$
$v = -(9.8 \frac{m}{s^2})(3 \text{ s})$
$v = -29.4 \frac{m}{s}$

2.10 $d = -\frac{1}{2} gt^2$
$= -\frac{1}{2} (9.8 \frac{m}{s^2})(1 \text{ s})^2$
$= -4.9 \text{ m}$

$d = -\frac{1}{2} gt^2$
$= -\frac{1}{2} (9.8 \frac{m}{s^2})(2 \text{ s})^2$
$= -19.6 \text{ m}$

2.11 because it is accelerating; because the velocity is increasing in each time interval

2.12 $F_J = \dfrac{Gm_J m_o}{r_J^2}$; G is a universal gravitational constant (it is the same for all objects), m_o is the mass of the object and does not change, but m_J and r_J refer to Jupiter's mass and radius and these differ from those of earth; therefore, F_J is different for Jupiter.

2.13 The gravitational force, or attraction, of the sun extends out into space far past the orbit of Pluto.

2.14 F gets small rapidly as d gets larger; however, although F will become very small it will theoretically never be equal to zero.

2.15 The forces from the earth and the moon are equal and opposite; therefore, the net force is zero.

III. SECTION THREE

3.1 $T = \dfrac{4\text{ s}}{10\text{ rev}} = .4$ s

$v = \dfrac{2\pi R}{T}$

$= \dfrac{2(3.14)(1\text{ m})}{0.4\text{ s}}$

$v = 15.7\ \dfrac{m}{s}$

3.2 $a = \dfrac{v^2}{R} = \dfrac{(15.7\ \frac{m}{s})^2}{1\text{ m}}$

$a = 246.5\ \dfrac{m}{s^2}$

or

$a = \dfrac{4\pi^2 R}{T^2} = \dfrac{4(3.14)^2(1\text{ m})}{(0.4\text{ s})^2}$

$a = 246.5\ \dfrac{m}{s^2}$

3.3 $T = \dfrac{1\text{ s}}{\frac{1}{4}\text{ rev}} = 4$ s

$v = \dfrac{2\pi R}{T}$

$R = \dfrac{vT}{2\pi} = \dfrac{(25\ \frac{m}{s})(4\text{ s})}{2(3.14)}$

$R = 16$ m

3.4 $a = \dfrac{v^2}{R} = \dfrac{(25\ \frac{m}{s})^2}{(16\text{ m})}$

$a = 39\ \dfrac{m}{sec^2}$

3.5 toward the center in all cases of uniform circular motion

3.6 $1.02 \times 10^3 \dfrac{m}{sec} \cdot$

$v = \sqrt{\dfrac{Gm_E}{R}} =$

$\sqrt{\dfrac{(6.67 \cdot 10^{-11}\frac{N \cdot m}{kg})(5.98 \cdot 10^{24}\text{kg})}{3.8 \times 10^8 \text{m}}}$

$v = \sqrt{10.50 \times 10^5 \dfrac{m^2}{sec^2}} = 1.02 \times 10^3 \dfrac{m}{sec}$

3.7 $F = ma = \dfrac{mv^2}{R}$

$= \dfrac{(2\text{ kg})(15.7\ \frac{m}{s})^2}{1\text{ m}}$

$F = 493$ N

or $F = ma$

$= (2\text{ kg})(246.5\ \dfrac{m}{s^2})$

$F = 493$ N

3.8 $F = ma = \dfrac{mv^2}{R}$

$v^2 = \dfrac{FR}{m}$

$v = \sqrt{\dfrac{FR}{m}}$

$= \sqrt{\dfrac{(4\text{ N})(2\text{ m})}{0.5\text{ kg}}}$

$v = 4\ \dfrac{m}{s}$

3.9 $a = \dfrac{v^2}{R}$

       $a = \dfrac{(4\frac{m}{s})^2}{2\ m}$

       $a = 8\frac{m}{s^2}$

3.10   A graph - depends on data

3.11   It should be close to a straight line with a positive slope.

3.12   A graph - depends on data

3.13   It should be close to a straight line, but with a different slope.

3.14   The mass halves $\frac{1}{T^2}$ are doubled because $m \propto F$, $2\,m \propto 2\,F$, and $\frac{1}{T^2} \propto F$; therefore, $2\,F \propto 2(\frac{1}{T^2})$. To keep $F \propto \frac{m}{T^2}$, a constant $F \propto \frac{2\,m}{2\,T^2}$.

3.15   Keeping the mass a constant is easy; just use one stopper. However, continuous adjustment of force would have to be made to keep the same T: a tedious job.

3.16   Force $\propto R$ (that is, a straight line on a graph of R versus number of washers).

IV.   SECTION FOUR

4.1   The reaction force is the raft against his feet.

4.2 $-(50\ \text{kg})(v) = (30\ \text{kg})(2\tfrac{m}{s})$

       $v = \dfrac{-60\ \frac{kg \cdot m}{s}}{50\ kg}$

       $v = -1.2\ \frac{m}{s}$ (to the left)

4.3 $(2\ \text{kg})(v) = (2\ \text{kg} + 1\ \text{kg})(\tfrac{-1m}{s})$

       $v = \dfrac{-3\ \frac{kg \cdot m}{s}}{2\ kg}$

       $v = -1.5\ \frac{m}{s}$ (to the left)

4.4   Nothing happens.

4.5   no

4.6   zero

4.7   zero

4.8   yes

4.9   yes for cases 4, 5, and 6

4.10   Frictional effects cause discrepancies; but, when the carts have equal masses, the effects cancel each other.

4.11   zero

4.12   zero

4.13   Total momentum after equals the total momentum before: zero.

4.14   yes

4.15   that it is a constant for the release height

4.16   They are almost equal.

4.17   yes

4.18   They are not equal.

4.19   They are almost equal.

4.20   yes

V.   SECTION FIVE

5.1   adult check

5.2   Areas are the same.

5.3   Areas are the same.

5.4   Areas are the same.

5.5   Areas are the same.

5.6   Areas are the same.

5.7   yes

5.8   Near the real focus, the triangle's altitude is long and its base is short. Half-way between extremes, the altitude is short and the base is long. The speed varies as the planet orbits.

5.9   false

5.10   false

5.11   true

5.12   b

5.13   b

5.14   c

5.15   c

5.16   a

5.17   d

5.18   retrograde

5.19   epicircular

5.20   heliocentric

5.21   geocentric

5.22   Ptolemy

5.23   a. Copernicus   (1473-1543)
       b. Newton   (1642-1727)
       c. Brahe   (1546-1601)
       d. Aristarchus (320-250 B.C.)
       e. Ptolemy   (c. 100-170)
       f. Galileo   (1564-1642)
       g. Aristotle   (384-322 B.C.)
       h. Kepler   (1571-1630)

5.24 $$\frac{R_A^{\,3}}{T_A^{\,2}} = \frac{R_B^{\,3}}{T_B^{\,2}}$$

$$\frac{(1\ au)^3}{(1\ year)^2} = \frac{(4\ au)^3}{T_B^{\,2}} = \frac{64\ au^3}{T_B^{\,2}}$$

$$T_B^{\,2} = 64\ years^2$$

$$T_B = 8\ years$$

5.25 $$\frac{R_m^3}{T_m^2} = \frac{R_s^3}{T_s^2}$$

$$R_s^3 = \frac{R_m^3 \cdot T_s^2}{T_m^2}$$

$$= \frac{(240{,}000\ mi)^3 (1\ day)^2}{(28\ day)^2}$$

$$R_s^3 = 17.63 \cdot 10^{12}\ mi^3$$

$$R_s = 2.6 \cdot 10^4\ mi = 26{,}000\ mi$$

1.1 $KE = \frac{1}{2}mv^2$ $(v_{60\ mph} = 3v_{20\ mph})$

$(v_{60\ mph})^2 = 9(v_{20\ mph})^2$

KE increases by a factor of 9

1.2 $F \cdot d = \frac{1}{2}mv^2$ $(v_{60\ mph} = 4v_{15\ mph})$

$(v_{60\ mph})^2 = 16(v_{15\ mph})^2$

KE increases by a factor of 16

$F \cdot d = 16\ KE$

since F does not change, d must increase by a factor of 16

1.3 $M = \frac{F}{a} = \frac{weight}{a} = \frac{3,200\ lb.}{32\ \frac{ft.}{sec.^2}} = 100$

slugs.

$30\ mph = 44\ \frac{ft.}{sec.}$

kinetic energy $= \frac{1}{2}mv^2$

$= \frac{1}{2}(100\ slugs)(44\ \frac{ft.}{sec.})^2$

$KE = 96,800\ ft. \cdot lb.$ or
$(9.68 \cdot 10^4\ ft. \cdot lb.)$

1.4 $15\ mph = \frac{1}{2}(30\ mph)$

$v^2_{15\ mph} = (\frac{1}{2})^2(v_{30\ mph})^2$

$= \frac{1}{4}(v_{30\ mph})^2$

$KE_{15\ mph} = \frac{1}{4}KE_{30\ mph}$

1.5 $Fd = \frac{1}{2}mv^2$

$(80N)(4m) = \frac{1}{2}(10\ kg)(v^2)$

$\frac{320\ N \cdot m}{5\ kg} = v^2$

$64\ \frac{m^2}{sec.^2} = v^2$

$8\ \frac{m}{sec.} = v$

1.6   The kinetic energy increases as the square of the velocity, which makes the car a more lethal object at the higher speed. Since velocity doubles, the kinetic energy increases by a factor of 4.

1.7 $PE = mgh$

$= (5\ kg)(9.8\ \frac{m}{sec.^2})(10\ m)$

$= 490\ \frac{kg \cdot m^2}{sec.^2}$

$PE = 490\ J$

1.8 $Work = Fd = mgh$
$Work = 490\ J$

1.9   The distance involved is 5 m (change in height, not the ramp length)

$Work = Fd = (mg)(d)$

$= (20\ kg)(9.8\ \frac{m}{sec.^2})(5\ m)$

$Work = 980\ J$

1.10 $PE = mgh = Fd$
$PE = 980\ J$

1.11   adult check

1.12
    a.   heat energy
    b.   nuclear power, electrical power
    c.   heat energy
    d.   heat energy, light energy
    e.   light energy, heat energy
    f.   heat energy, light energy
       chemical energy
    g.   kinetic energy
    h.   potential energy, chemical energy
    i.   potential energy, chemical energy
    j.   potential energy

1.13   geothermal energy, nuclear energy, and tidal energy

1.14
    a.   potential energy
    b.   potential energy
    c.   kinetic energy
    d.   kinetic energy
    e.   potential energy
    f.   potential energy

2.1   at point E, the bottom of the swing

2.2   at point A, the top of the swing

2.3   A, where it is stopped

2.4   at point E

2.5 $\dfrac{B}{A} = \dfrac{15}{20} = \dfrac{3}{4}$

 $\dfrac{3}{4} \cdot 12\ J = 9\ J$

2.6   a. 6 J
 b. 3 J
 c. 0 J

2.7   total energy = PE + KE
 12 J = 9 J + KE
 KE = 12 J - 9 J
 KE = 3 J

2.8   a. 6 J
 b. 9 J
 c. 12 J
 d. 0 J

2.9   The total energy at any point along the arc of swing of the pendulum is always equal to 12 joules.

2.10 Kinetic energy will increase from 0 J to 12 J and potential energy will decrease from 12 J to 0 J.

2.11 PE = mgh = $(10\ kg)(9.8\ \frac{m}{sec.^2})(320\ m)$
 PE = 31,360 J

2.12 KE = $\frac{1}{2}mv^2$ = 0 because v = 0

2.13 $\frac{1}{2}mv^2$ = mgh
 $v^2 = \dfrac{mgh}{\frac{1}{2}m} = \dfrac{(9.8\ \frac{m}{sec.^2})(320\ m)}{\frac{1}{2}}$
 $v^2 = 6,300\ \dfrac{m^2}{sec.^2}$
 $v = 80\ \dfrac{m}{sec.}$ (approximately)

2.14 $\frac{1}{2}mv^2$ = mgh
 $\frac{1}{2}v^2$ = gh

 No, since mass appears on both sides of the equation, it can be cancelled from both sides.

2.15 The acceleration due to gravity depends on the planet's gravity and not on the object being dropped. All objects attain the same speed over the same distance.

Sample data: 2.16-2.23

2.16 Examples:
 a. about 50
 b. about 5

2.17 Example:
 $\dfrac{6}{10}$sec.

2.18 Example:

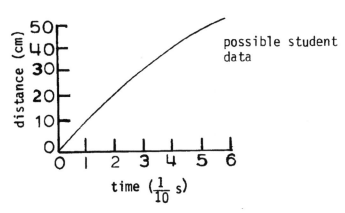

possible student data

2.19 adult check

2.20 Examples:
 a. about 5 cm
 b. about 0.05 m

2.21 Example:
 If the brick has a mass of 1 kg and h = 0.05 m,
 PE = mgh
  = $(1\ kg)(9.8\ \frac{m}{sec.^2})(0.05\ m)$
 PE = 0.49 J

123

2.22   Example:

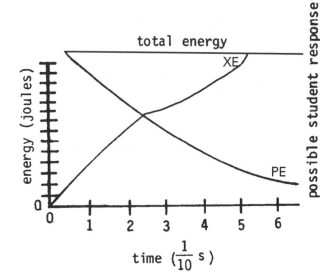

total energy

XE

PE

energy (joules)

0

0   1   2   3   4   5   6

time ($\frac{1}{10}$ s)

possible student response

2.23   a. decreases
         b. increases
         c. The total energy is equal to
             the potential plus kinetic
             energy and is constant.
         d. nearly so
         e. measurement error, deter-
             mination of center of swing,
             friction between the tape
             and timer, height measurement,
             calibration error, wind resis-
             tance, inaccurate slope
             determination

2.24   E = mgh

$$= (1{,}000 \text{ kg})(9.8 \ \frac{m}{sec.^2})(10 \text{ m})$$

$$= 9.8 \cdot 10^4 \text{ J for both motors}$$

2.25   a. Motor #1

$$P = \frac{\Delta E}{\Delta t}$$

$$= \frac{9.8 \cdot 10^4 \text{ J}}{5 \text{ sec.}}$$

$$= 1.96 \cdot 10^4 \text{ watts}$$

         b. Motor #2

$$P = \frac{\Delta E}{\Delta t}$$

$$= \frac{9.8 \cdot 10^4 \text{ J}}{10 \text{ sec.}}$$

$$P = 0.98 \cdot 10^4 \text{ watts}$$

2.26 $P = \dfrac{E}{t} = \dfrac{F \cdot d}{t}$

$$= \frac{(150 \text{ 1b.})(10 \text{ ft.})}{5 \text{ sec.}}$$

$$= 300 \text{ ft.} \cdot \frac{1b.}{sec.}$$

$$P = \frac{300 \ \frac{ft. \cdot 1b.}{sec.}}{550} = 0.55 \text{ hp}$$

2.27   efficiency $= \dfrac{4{,}000 \text{ J}}{16{,}000 \text{ J}} \cdot 100\%$

efficiency = 25%

2.28   efficiency $= \dfrac{90 \text{ J}}{100 \text{ J}} \cdot 100\%$

$$= 90\%$$

2.29   100% - 90% = 10% or 10 joules
Sample data :   2.30 - 2.37
2.30   Hint:
        $d_{50 \text{ g}}$ is 4 times longer than

        $d_{200 \text{ g}}$

2.31   Hint:
        $d_{100 \text{ g}}$ is 3 times longer than

        $d_{300 \text{ g}}$

2.32   The ratios of distance and mass
        are inverse (case #1 masses are
        4:1, distances 1:4; case #2 masses
        are 3:1, distances are 1:3). Mass
        times distance on one side equals
        mass times distance on the other
        ($m_1 \ d_1 = m_2 \ d_2$).

2.33   a. and b.
        Hint: will be equal.

2.34   Yes, it does; ratios are 1:1 for
        mass and distance or $m_1 \ d_1 = m_2 \ d_2$.

2.35   adult check

2.36   ratios do not hold

2.37 $m_1 \cdot d_1 + m_2 \cdot d_2 = m_3 \cdot d_3$ is the

        general statement.

2.38   Hint: answers will be close to 4

2.39   Hint: answers will be close to 99%

2.40   Only the fulcrum can cause
       frictional losses.

2.41   No, because work equals force
       times distance. Less force means
       more distance. To lift the 200-g
       mass 1 cm, the 50-g mass had to
       move 4 cm.

2.42   No. 105% efficiency means that
       you are getting more work out than
       you put in. Clearly a physical
       impossibility.

III. SECTION THREE

3.1   a. $333°K$
       b. $27°C$
       c. $212°F$
       d. $473°K$

3.2   heat $= m\Delta t$
            $= (4\ kg)(45°C - 25°C)$
            $= (4\ kg)(20°C)$
       heat $= 80\ kcal$ or $80\ Cal$

3.3   Because the specific heat of water
       is so much greater than that of
       lead, 1.00 compared to 0.03 or a
       ratio of 33:1, the 300° of the lead
       is not enough to overcome this
       factor.

3.4   a

3.5   b

3.6   b

3.7   c

3.8   d

3.9   Sufficient heat must be added to
       solid copper to cause the atoms
       to have vibrational, rotational,
       and translational motion.

3.10   heat $= (m)(C)(\Delta t)$
            $= (2\ kg)(.09)(100\ C)$
       heat $= 18\ kcal$

3.11   heat alumininum loss = heat water
       gain
       $(m_{A1})(C_{A1})(\Delta t_{A1}) =$
       $(M_{H_2O})(C_{H_2O})(\Delta t_{H_2O})$
       $(30\ kg)(.22)(20°C) = (20\ kg)(1)(\Delta t)$
       $\dfrac{(30\ kg)(.22)(20°C)}{20\ kg} = \Delta t$
       $\Delta t = 6.6°C$

3.12   heat $= (m)(C_{ice})(\ t)$
       $\Delta t = \dfrac{heat}{m \cdot C_{ice}}$
       $\Delta t = \dfrac{10\ cal}{(2g)(.5)}$
       $\Delta t = 10°C = t_f - t_i$
       $t_f = \Delta t + t_i$
       $t_f = 10°C + (-30°C)$
       $t_f = -20°C$

3.13   heat $= (m)(C)(\Delta t) + (m)(L_f)$
            $= (3\ kg)(0.09)(1,000°C) +$
              $(3\ kg)(51\ \frac{kcal}{kg})$
            $= 270\ kcal + 153\ kcal$
       heat $= 423\ kcal$

3.14   heat $= (m)(C)(\Delta t)$
            $= (10\ kg)(0.5)(-273°C - (-23°C))$
            $= (10\ kg)(0.5)(250°C)$
            $= 1,250\ kcal$

3.15   heat $= (m)(C)(\Delta t) + (m)(L_f) +$
              $(m)(C)(\Delta t)$
            $= (100\ kg)(1)(60°C)$ water to
              freezing $+ (100\ kg)(80\ \frac{kcal}{kg})$
              water to ice $+$
              $(100\ kg)(0.5)(273°)$ ice to
              absolute zero
       heat $= 27,650\ kcal$

Sample data for 3.16-3.28

3.16 a.   50 g
         b.   250 g
         c.   200 g
         d.   25°g
         e.   0°C
         f.   5°C
         g.   300 g
         h.   50 g
         i. $.22 \frac{cal}{g \cdot °C}$

3.17 0°C

3.18 20°C

3.19 20°C

3.20 5°C

3.21 heat = (200 g)(20°C)
       heat = 4,000 cal

3.22 heat = (50 g)(.22)(20°C)
       heat = 220 cal

3.23 4,220

3.24 250

3.25 3,970

3.26 79

3.27 comparison of student answer and
       $80 \frac{cal}{g}$

3.28 heat lost by the thermometer,
       some of the ice may have melted
       prior to mixing, imperfect
       insulation.

3.29 No. Water boils at 100°C at sea
       level. More heat under the pan
       will only evaporate the water
       faster at 100°C.

3.30 because that gaseous phase has
       more heat than does the liquid
       phase, even at the same
       temperature.

3.31 $heat = (m_{H_2O})(C_{H_2O})(\Delta t) + (m)(L_v) +$
       $(m_{steam})(C_{steam})(\Delta t)$
       $= (10 \text{ g})(1)(100° - 70°) +$
       $(10 \text{ g})(540 \frac{cal}{g}) +$
       $(10 \text{ g})(0.48)(110° - 100°)$
      $heat = 300 \text{ cal} + 5,400 \text{ cal} +$
       $48.0 \text{ cal} = 5,748 \text{ cal}$
       5.75 kcal

3.32 $heat = (m)(C)(\Delta t) + (m)(L_v)$
       $= (10 \text{ kg})(.11)(2,740°C -$
       $2,640°C) + (10 \text{ kg})(1,620 \frac{kcal}{kg})$
       $= (10 \text{ kg})(.11)(100°C) +$
       16,200 kcal
      $heat = (110 + 16,200) \text{ kcal} =$
       16,310 kcal

3.33 $heat = (200 \text{ g})(50°C - 20°C)$
       $= (200 \text{ g})(30°C)$
      $heat = 6,000 \text{ cal}$

3.34 $heat = (50 \text{ g})(.22)(30°C)$
       heat = 330 cal

3.35 heat = 6,000 cal + 330 cal =
       6,330 cal

3.36 6,330 cal

3.37 $heat = (m)(C)(\Delta t)$
       $= (11 \text{ g})(1)(100°C - 50°C)$
       = 550 cal

3.38 6,330 cal - 550 cal = 5,780 cal

3.39 $\frac{5,780 \text{ cal}}{11 \text{ g}} = 525.5 \frac{cal}{g}$

3.40 not only steam but also water
       (condensed steam) entered the
       water, the thermometer gained
       energy, errors in mass and
       temperature readings

3.41 some condensation of the steam
       along the short rubber hose from
       the trap to the container

3.42   Heat (solar) energy evaporates water from the oceans. Rain trapped behind dams in the form of potential energy is converted into kinetic energy to turn turbines creating electrical energy.

3.43   Heat energy from coal, gas, oil, or electricty heats water into steam. As the steam travels through the radiators it releases heat to the metal which in turn heats air in the house.

3.44   The kinetic energy is transformed into heat energy in the brakes and is dissipated.

3.45   a. The mechanical energy is easy to observe in the motion of the motor. Heat given off is felt by the warm air.
         b. Since heat energy is lost, the efficiency is less than 100%.

3.46   efficiency $= \dfrac{T_h - T_c}{T_h} \cdot 100\%$

$= \dfrac{400°K - 360°K}{400°K} \cdot 100\%$

$= 10\%$

3.47   efficiency $= \dfrac{T_h - T_c}{T_h} \cdot 100\%$

$= \dfrac{(270 + 273) - (180 + 273)}{(270 + 273)} \cdot 100\%$

efficiency $= \dfrac{90}{543} \cdot 100\% = 16.6\%$

3.48   efficiency $= \dfrac{T_h - T_c}{T_h} \cdot 100\%$

$= \dfrac{600°K - 400°K}{600°K} \cdot 100\%$

$= \dfrac{200°K}{600°K} \cdot 100\%$

$= 33\tfrac{1}{3}\%$

3.49   efficiency $= \dfrac{T_h - T_c}{T_h}$

$T_c = T_h - T_h \cdot$ efficiency

$T_c = 300 - 100 = 200°K$

3.50   Efficiencies are the same. Although the temperature differences vary, the ratios of temperature difference to hot temperature are the same.

1.1 the motion of your hand

1.2 a long pulse

1.3 a short pulse

1.4 not by much; some friction is encountered with the floor

1.5 not by much; some friction is encountered with the floor

1.6 As the stretch increased, the velocity increased.

1.7 a. 1.5 meters

   b. 8 meters

   c. 4 sec.

   d. $\frac{1}{4}$ Hz (or $\frac{cycles}{sec.}$)

   e. 2 $\frac{m}{sec.}$

1.8 a. $\frac{2}{3}$ m

   b. 0.5 Hz

   c. $T = \frac{1}{f}$

   $= \frac{1}{0.5 \, Hz} = 2$ sec.

1.9 a. $\frac{1}{3}$ Hz

   b. $v = f\lambda$

   $\lambda = \frac{v}{f} = \frac{24 \frac{m}{sec.}}{\frac{1}{3} \, Hz}$

   $\lambda = 72$ m

   c. No, the amplitude is not a function of the velocity, frequency, or wavelength.

1.10 Yes, they do.

1.11 yes

1.12 yes

1.13 yes, between where the coils are close together

1.14 they go back to their original position

1.15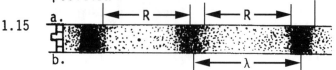

1.16 a. $T = \frac{1}{f} = \frac{1}{660 \, Hz} =$ sec.

   or 0.0015 sec.

   b. $v = f\lambda$

   $= (660 Hz)(\frac{1}{2}m)$

   $= 330 \frac{m}{sec.}$

1.17 a. $v = f\lambda$

   $f = \frac{v}{\lambda} = \frac{330 \frac{m}{sec.}}{33 \, m}$

   $f = 10$ Hz

   b. $T = \frac{1}{f} = \frac{1}{10}$ sec.

1.18 adult check

II. SECTION TWO

2.1 back along the path of the incident pulses

2.2 The effect is to turn the reflected pulses 90° to the incident pulses.

2.3 They are equal.

2.4 Reflected pulse returns on the opposite side of the Slinky.

2.5 The reflected pulse returns on the same side as the incident pulse.

2.6 no

2.7 yes

2.8 it decreases

2.9 shallow water

2.10 yes

2.11 deep water

2.12 yes

2.13 adult check

2.14 Varying depths and varying tensions represent differences in media.

2.15 When a wave traveling from a low-velocity medium to a high-velocity medium encounters that medium at the critical angle, the wave is reflected and no portion of the wave is transmitted.

2.16 yes

2.17 no

2.18 no

2.19 no

2.20 a. crest
b. trough
c. crest
d. trough

2.21 a. trough
b. trough
c. trough
d. trough

2.22 The effect is sharpest when the opening is smaller than the wavelength.

2.23 the larger wavelengths

2.24 Diffraction occurs if the obstacle is larger than the wavelength of the wave.

2.25 the amplitude increases

2.26 The waves do not bounce off each other, but they go through each other. Upon meeting they form a different shape then reappear after crossing.

2.27 yes

2.28 yes

2.29 from one node to the second full node away; the distance between three consecutive nodes

2.30 the wavelength decreases

2.31 The velocity does not change.

2.32 $v = f\lambda$
$= (4 \text{ Hz}) (2.5 \text{ m}) (2)$
$= 20 \frac{\text{m}}{\text{sec.}}$

2.33 $v = f\lambda$
$f = \frac{v}{\lambda}$
$= \frac{20 \frac{\text{cm}}{\text{sec.}}}{4 \text{ cm}}$
$= 5 \text{ Hz}$

2.34 they increase

2.35 large separation

2.36 adult check

2.37 adult check

2.38 adult check

2.39 adult check

2.40 $\lambda = \frac{dX}{L} \div (n - \frac{1}{2})$

2.41 antinodes

2.42   a. $\dfrac{(n - \frac{1}{2})\lambda}{d} = \dfrac{X}{L}$

$\dfrac{(n - \frac{1}{2})\lambda}{1,000 \text{ m}} = \dfrac{2,000 \text{ m}}{8,000 \text{ m}}$

$\dfrac{\frac{1}{2}\lambda}{1,000 \text{ m}} = \dfrac{1}{4}$

$\frac{1}{2}\lambda = 250 \text{ m}$

$\lambda = 500 \text{ m}$

b. $v = f\lambda$

$\lambda = \dfrac{v}{f}$

$\lambda = \dfrac{3 \cdot 10^8 \frac{\text{m}}{\text{sec.}}}{6 \cdot 10^5 \text{ Hz}}$

$\lambda = 500 \text{ m}$

c. No, the radio's wavelength places your house along its first nodal line.

2.43   a. $\dfrac{(n - \frac{1}{2})\lambda}{d} = \dfrac{X}{L}$

$\dfrac{(2 - \frac{1}{2})\lambda}{1 \text{ m}} = \dfrac{2 \text{ m}}{4 \text{ m}}$

$\dfrac{\frac{3}{2}\lambda}{1 \text{ m}} = \dfrac{1}{2}$

$\frac{3}{2}\lambda = \frac{1}{2} \text{ m}$

$\left(\frac{2}{3}\right)\left(\frac{3}{2}\lambda\right) = \frac{2}{3}\left(\frac{1}{2} \text{ m}\right)$

$\lambda = \frac{1}{3} \text{ m}$

b. $v = f\lambda$

$f = \dfrac{v}{\lambda}$

$f = \dfrac{330 \text{ m}}{\frac{1}{3} \text{ m}}$

$f = 990 \text{ Hz}$

2.44 $\dfrac{(n - \frac{1}{2})\lambda}{d} = \dfrac{X}{L}$

$\dfrac{(1 - \frac{1}{2})\lambda}{3 \text{ cm}} = \dfrac{4 \text{ cm}}{12 \text{ cm}}$

$\dfrac{\frac{1}{2}\lambda}{3 \text{ cm}} = \dfrac{1}{3}$

$\frac{1}{2}\lambda = 1 \text{ cm}$

$\lambda = 2 \text{ cm}$

III.   SECTION THREE

3.1   6 beats/sec.

3.2   480 Hz + 4 Hz = 484 Hz
480 Hz - 4 Hz = 476 Hz

470 Hz + 6 Hz = 476 Hz
470 Hz - 6 Hz = 464 Hz
unknown piano key = 476 Hz

3.3   teacher check

3.4   they become shorter

3.5   they become longer

3.6   The greater the difference in velocities, the more acute will be the cone.

3.7-3.11 Examples:

3.7   512 Hz

3.8   20° C

3.9   16 cm for 512 Hz

3.10   50 cm for 512 Hz

3.11 $\lambda = 2(L_2 - L_1)$
2(50 cm - 16 cm) = 68 cm

3.12   Be sure to change length to meters.
$v = (512 \text{ Hz})(0.68 \text{ m})$
$= 348 \dfrac{\text{m}}{\text{sec.}}$

130

3.13 $v = 330 \frac{m}{sec.} + (.6)(20° C)\frac{m}{sec.}$

        $v = (330 + 12)\frac{m}{sec.}$

3.14   Using $v = 330 + .6\ T\frac{m}{sec.}$ is more accurate.

3.15   temperature readings in the tube are cooler due to cold water, inaccurate measure lengths of L_1 and L_2

3.16   Determine the velocity using the temperature equation and divide by the wave length determined from the experiment.

1.1 adult check

1.2 It measured man's reaction time, and it proved that the speed of light was very fast.

1.3 The symbol c is used to denote the velocity of light in a vacuum, and is equal to $3 \cdot 10^8 \frac{m}{sec.}$ or $1.86 \cdot 10^5 \frac{mi.}{sec.}$

1.4 His experiment accurately measured the speed of light in air. It earned him the Nobel prize in 1907 and he became the first American physicist to receive it.

1.5 It would show that the speed of light will be less than $3 \cdot 10^8 \frac{m}{sec.}$, or $1.86 \cdot 10^5 \frac{mi.}{sec.}$

1.6 The light shines directly back.

1.7 They reflect in the same way.

1.8 adult check

1.9 adult check

1.10 The angles are equal.

1.11 They were equal.

1.12 The angle of incidence equals the angle of reflection.

1.13 No, the ball bearing reflects like light reflects.

1.14 The wave slowed down.

1.15 Yes, the angle of incidence is the larger angle.

1.16 The air is the high-velocity medium.

1.17 adult check

1.18 should be less than 1.17

1.19 The angle decreases or bends toward the normal.

1.20 The ray of light bends toward the normal.

1.21 at the table surface

1.22 The angle decreased in the high-velocity medium.

1.23 Light behaves like a wave.

1.24 $n = \frac{c}{v}$

$n = \dfrac{3 \cdot 10^8 \frac{m}{sec.}}{2.25 \cdot 10^8 \frac{m}{sec.}}$

$n = 1\frac{1}{3}$

1.25 $n = \frac{c}{v}, \; v = \frac{c}{n}$

$v = \dfrac{3 \cdot 10^8 \frac{m}{sec.}}{1.8}$

$v = 1.67 \cdot 10^8 \frac{m}{sec.}$

1.26 $n = \dfrac{sin\ i}{sin\ r} = \dfrac{sin\ 30°}{sin\ 22°}$

$n = \dfrac{.5000}{.3746} = 1.33$

1.27 $n = \dfrac{sin\ i}{sin\ r}$

$sin\ r = \dfrac{sin\ i}{n}$

$sin\ r = \dfrac{sin\ 45°}{1.33} = \dfrac{.7071}{1.33}$

$sin\ r = .5317$

$r = 32.1°$

1.28   should be close to 1.33

1.29   1.33

1.30   varies with student's answer to 1.28

1.31   yes, it is the same

1.32   the students should be able to

1.33   yes, they do

1.34   yes, it does

1.35   90°

1.36   Glare diminished with a vertical orientation.

1.37   Reflected light is partially polarized.

1.38   You see the object.

1.39   You see the object.

1.40   You see nothing, no light gets through.

1.41   No, it does not.

1.42   The object is visible **again**.

1.43   Yes, it could get through the filters.

1.44   No, it would be stopped by one of the filters.

1.45   Light is a transverse wave.

1.46   false

1.47   false

1.48   true

1.49   true

1.50   true

1.51   false

1.52   true

1.53   false

1.54   true

1.55   true

1.56   true

1.57   true

II.   SECTION TWO

2.1   They are equal.

2.2   yes

2.3   about the same size

2.4   No, Q is behind the mirror and no light comes from there to the eye.

2.5   three images, for there are three "mirror rooms "

2.6   false

2.7   true

2.8   true

2.9   false

2.10   true

2.11   a. $\dfrac{H_o}{H_i} = \dfrac{S_o}{f}$

$\dfrac{6 \text{ cm}}{H_i} = \dfrac{10 \text{ cm}}{5 \text{ cm}}$

$6 \text{ cm} = 2 \, H_i$

$H_i = 3 \text{ cm}$

b. $\dfrac{H_o}{H_i} = \dfrac{f}{S_i}$

$\dfrac{6 \text{ cm}}{3 \text{ cm}} = \dfrac{5 \text{ cm}}{S_i}$

$2 \, S_i = 5 \text{ cm}$

$S_i = 2.5 \text{ cm}$

2.12   a. $\dfrac{H_o}{H_i} = \dfrac{S_o}{f}$

$$\dfrac{3 \text{ cm}}{H_i} = \dfrac{6 \text{ cm}}{5 \text{ cm}}$$

$$6 \, H_i = (3 \text{ cm})(5)$$

$$H_i = 2.5 \text{ cm}$$

    b. $\dfrac{H_o}{H_i} = \dfrac{f}{S_i}$

$$\dfrac{3 \text{ cm}}{2.5 \text{ cm}} = \dfrac{5 \text{ cm}}{S_i}$$

$$3 \, S_i = (5)(2.5 \text{ cm})$$

$$S_i = 4.2 \text{ cm}$$

2.13   yes, they do

2.14   yes

2.15   The wave reflects parallel.

2.16   yes, it does

2.17   adult check

2.18   adult check

2.19   real image and inverted

2.20
$$S_o S_i = f^2$$
$$(8 \text{ m})(2 \text{ m}) = f^2$$
$$16 \text{ m}^2 = f^2$$
$$4 \text{ m} = f$$

2.21 $\dfrac{H_o}{H_i} = \dfrac{S_o}{f}$

$$\dfrac{0.5 \text{ m}}{H_i} = \dfrac{8 \text{ m}}{4 \text{ m}}$$

$$2 \, H_i = 0.5 \text{ m}$$

$$H_i = 0.25 \text{ m}$$

2.22   Close objects have larger images.

2.23   They are inverted unless they are very close; then they are erect.

2.24   The position and size of the image change.

2.25   at infinity

2.26   It is a constant equal to f^2.

2.27   It equals f, the focal length.

2.28   a straight line

2.29   adult check

2.30   The images are always virtual, erect, and diminished.

III.   SECTION THREE

3.1   fine lines

3.2   They are parallel.

3.3   adult check

3.4   adult check

3.5   adult check

3.6   adult check

3.7   adult check

3.8   adult check

3.9   blue light

3.10   Some discrepancy is likely.

3.11   the answer for the blue light width

3.12 $4.3 \cdot 10^{14}$ Hz

3.13 $6.2 \cdot 10^{14}$ Hz

3.14   because you decrease the effect of human error

3.15   adult check

3.16   adult check

3.17   adult check

3.18   close to $7 \cdot 10^{-7}$ m

3.19   close to $4.3 \cdot 10^{14}$ m

3.20   It should be at least the same power of 10.

3.21   because red light has a large variation going from infrared to nearly orange

3.22   It is a smaller pattern.

3.23   Since $c = 3 \times 10^8 \frac{m}{sec.}$ and frequency of blue light is larger than red light, the wavelength of blue light must be smaller for $f\lambda = c$.

3.24   It gave evidence for the particle nature of light.

3.25   interference, diffraction, and polarization

3.26   The wave nature of light is a probability statement of where photons are going to be.

1.1 Charges build up as clothes rub against each other and against the tub.

1.2 Some fabrics are better insulators than others.

1.3 c

1.4 d

1.5 Benjamin Franklin

1.6 two

1.7 opposite

1.8 Either order:
a. positively
b. negatively

1.9 false

1.10 true

1.11 false

1.12 true

1.13 true

1.14 removing electrons

1.15 free electrons

1.16 outer shells

1.17 b

1.18 b

1.19 The ball should be repelled.

1.20 It is a repelling force.

1.21 The ball should be repelled.

1.22 It is a repelling force.

1.23 The ball should be attracted.

1.24 It is a force of attraction.

1.25 increases

1.26 decrease

1.27 a. charges
b. separation
c. force

1.28 unlike

1.29 inversely

1.30 $F = K\dfrac{Q_1Q_2}{r^2} = \left(\dfrac{9 \cdot 10^9 Nm^2}{c^2}\right)$

$\dfrac{(20 \cdot 10^{-6}c)(30 \cdot 10^{-6}c)}{(3m)^2}$

$= \left(\dfrac{9 \cdot 10^9 Nm^1}{c^2}\right)$

$\dfrac{(20 \cdot 10^{-6})(30 \cdot 10^{-6})c^2}{9m^2}$

$= 600 \cdot 10^9 \cdot 10^{-6} \cdot 10^{-6} N$

$= 0.600N$

1.31 $F = K\dfrac{Q_1Q_2}{r^2} = \left(9 \cdot 10^9 \dfrac{Nm^2}{c^2}\right)$

$\left(\dfrac{(10 \cdot 10^{-6}c)(-15 \cdot 10^{-6}c)}{(6m)^2}\right)$

$= \left(9 \cdot 10^9 \dfrac{Nm^2}{c^2}\right)\left(\dfrac{-150 \cdot 10^{-12}c^2}{36m^2}\right)$

$= \dfrac{(9)(-150) \cdot 10^{-3}N}{36}$

$= 37.5 \cdot 10^{-3}N$

$= -0.0375N$

1.32 b

1.33 c

1.34 a

1.35 a

1.36 "For by Him were all things created, that are in heaven and that are in earth, visible and invisible, whether they be thrones, or dominions, or principalities, or powers: all things were created by Him and for Him."

1.37   by Him all things are held
       together

1.38   All things were created by and for
       Him.

1.39   c

1.40   b

1.41   false

1.42   true

1.43   false

1.44   a conductor (or wire)

1.45   electrons

1.46   conductor

II. SECTION TWO

2.1   [Let: r_1 = first distance (1 m);
       $r_2 = \frac{1}{2}r_1$ = second distance (0.5 m)]

$$F_1 \propto \frac{1}{(r_1)^2} \qquad F_2 \propto \frac{1}{(\frac{1}{2}r_1)^2}$$

$$\frac{F_2}{F_1} = \frac{\frac{1}{(\frac{1}{2}r_1)^2}}{\frac{1}{(r_1)^2}} = \frac{(r_1)^2}{(\frac{1}{2}r_1)^2} = \frac{(r_1)^2}{\frac{1}{4}(r_1)^2} = \frac{4}{1}$$

$$4F_1 = F_2$$

$$\therefore 4(0.68N) = F_2$$

$$2.72N = F_2$$

2.2 $E = \frac{F}{q} = \frac{6.2N}{1 \cdot 10^{-6}c} = 6.2 \times 10^6 N/c$

2.3   electric field

2.4   Coulomb's

2.5   inversely

2.6   a.

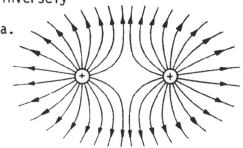

2.6   b.

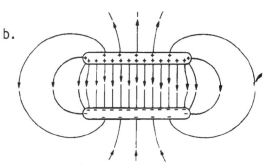

2.7   Either order:
       a. magnitude (size)
       b. direction

2.8   vectorially

2.9

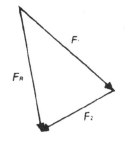

2.10   lightning

2.11   vertical

2.12   true

2.13   false

2.14   false

2.15   true

III. SECTION THREE

3.1   a.

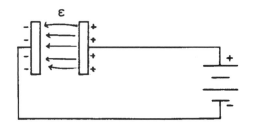

       b. no
       c. The positive charge derives
           from a deficit of electrons,
           not from an excess of free
           positive particles.

3.2   true

3.3   false

3.4   true

3.5   true

3.6 $E = \dfrac{v}{d} = \dfrac{12 \text{ volts}}{3 \text{ cm}}$

       $E = 4 \dfrac{\text{volts}}{\text{cm}}$

3.7 $1\frac{1}{3} \dfrac{\text{volts}}{\text{cm}}$

3.8   a. 12
       b. It is dead (without signs of life).

3.9   adult check

3.10   stored

3.11   a. field
       b. negatively

3.12   electrical energy

3.13   a. capacitance
       b. potential

3.14   square

3.15   decrease

3.16   true

3.17   true

3.18   true

3.19   true

3.20   false

3.21   true

3.22   Either order:
       a. Battery stores chemical energy, capacitor stores electric energy.
       b. Battery is capable of continuous current, capacitor is not.

3.23   Either order:
       a. both maintain a potential
       b. a field

3.24   true

3.25   true

3.26   false

3.27   false

1.1 Volta

1.2 steady

1.3 a. negative
    b. positive

1.4 electrons

1.5 adult check

1.6 true

1.7 true

1.8 false

1.9 true

1.10 false

1.11 An electric current is induced in a wire that is moving through a magnetic field.

1.12 b

1.13 b

1.14 true

1.15 false

1.16 true

1.17 false

1.18 true

1.19 $G = \sigma\frac{A}{l}$

$G = (0.7 \text{ unit} - \text{cm}^{-1})(\frac{2 \text{ cm}^2}{9 \text{ cm}})$

$G = 0.15$

1.20 $G = \sigma\frac{A}{l}$

$\sigma = \frac{Gl}{A} = \frac{(0.05 \text{ units})(15 \text{ cm})}{1.5 \text{ cm}^2}$

$\sigma = 1.5 \text{ units} - \text{cm}^{-1}$

1.21 b

1.22 b

1.23 a

1.24 b

1.25 positive charges

1.26 resistance

1.27 high

II. SECTION TWO

2.1 very low

2.2 resistance

2.3 semiconductor

2.4 free electrons

2.5 1 cm

2.6 false

2.7 true

2.8 false

2.9 true

2.10 true

2.11 a. $R = \rho\frac{1}{A} = (2.2 \cdot 10^{-5} \text{ ohm-cm})$

$(\frac{10 \text{ cm}}{0.1 \text{ cm}^2})$

$R = 2.2 \cdot 10^{-3} \text{ ohm}$

b. $R = \rho\frac{1}{A} = (1.63 \cdot 10^{-6} \text{ ohm-cm})$

$(\frac{10 \text{ cm}}{1.0 \text{ cm}^2})$

$R = 1.63 \cdot 10^{-4} \text{ ohms}$

III. SECTION THREE

3.1 constant or resistance

3.2 ohm

3.3 5

3.4 0.5

3.5 a. $E = IR$
   b. $R = \frac{E}{I}$
   c. $I = \frac{E}{R}$

3.6 ampere

3.7 volt

3.8 ohm

3.9 a. $R_T = R_1 + R_2 + R_3$
      $= 7\Omega + 6\Omega + 11\Omega$
      $= 24\Omega$
   b. $I = \frac{E}{R_T} = \frac{12 \text{ V}}{24\Omega} = 0.5 \text{ amps}$
   c. $I = \frac{E}{R_T} = \frac{24 \text{ V}}{7\Omega + 11\Omega}$
      $= \frac{24 \text{ V}}{18 \text{ }\Omega} = 1\frac{1}{3} \text{ amps}$

3.10 a. $I = 0.5 \text{ amp}$
    b. $V_1 = 3 \text{ volts}$
    c. $V_2 = 4 \text{ volts}$
    d. $V_3 = 5 \text{ volts}$
    e. $V_1 + V_2 + V_3 = 12 \text{ volts}$

3.11 a. $I = \frac{E}{R_T} = \frac{E}{R_1 + R_2 + R_3} = \frac{24 \text{ V}}{48\Omega}$
      $= 0.5 \text{ amps}$
      $P_1 = I^2 R_1 = (0.25)(8\Omega)$
      $= 2 \text{ watts}$
    b. $P_2 = I^2 R_2 = (0.25)(12\Omega)$
      $= 3 \text{ watts}$
    c. $P_3 = I^2 R_3 = (0.25)(28\Omega)$
      $= 7 \text{ watts}$
    d. $P_{total} = P_1 + P_2 + P_3$
      $= (2 + 3 + 7) \text{ watts}$
      $= 12 \text{ watts}$
      or
      $P_{circuit} = \frac{E^2}{R_T} = \frac{(24 \text{ V})}{48\Omega}$
      $= 12 \text{ watts}$

3.12 a. 2
    b. 4
    c. $1\frac{1}{3}$
    d. 48
    e. 96
    f. 32
    g. $7\frac{1}{3}$
    h. 176

1.1   c

1.2   c

1.3   a

1.4   b

1.5   a

1.6   a

1.7   adult check

1.8   adult check

1.9   adult check

1.10   adult check

1.11   adult check

1.12   adult check

1.13   at the poles

1.14   yes

1.15   no

1.16   Coulumb's law

1.17   alike

1.18   four

1.19   inverse

1.20   magnetic

1.21   force

1.22   zero

1.23   length

1.24   b

1.25   a

1.26 $F = qvB = q\frac{d}{t}B$

$F = \frac{q}{t}dB$

$F = ILB$ or BIL

II. SECTION TWO

2.1   b

2.2   a

2.3   b

2.4   c

2.5   a

2.6   perpendicular

2.7   perpendicular, but opposite the direction in 2.6.

2.8   It tries to point into the table.

2.9   yes

2.10   The needle follows circular paths around the wire.

2.11   concentric

2.12   magnetism

2.13   a. current
       b. distance

2.14   left-hand rule

2.15   zero

2.16   in opposite directions

2.17   b

2.18   magnet

2.19   battery

2.20   induction

2.21   ammeter

2.22   voltage or potential

2.23   work or energy

2.24   flux

2.25   transformer

2.26   c

2.27   b

2.28   a

2.29   a. induced emf
        b. magnetic field
        c. area of the conducting loop
        d. time

2.30   energy = charge x voltage
        $E = q \times V = 2 \text{ coul} \times 40.0V$
        $E = 80 \text{ joules}$

2.31 $W = Q\epsilon$
        $P = \dfrac{W}{t} = \dfrac{Q}{t}\epsilon \text{ or } \dfrac{Q}{t}V$
        $P = IV$

III.   SECTION THREE

3.1   a. $qvB_{\perp}$ or BIL
       b. charge
       c. velocity
       d. perpendicular magnetic
          field component

3.2 $\dfrac{E}{B}$

3.3   a. cathode
       b. control grid
       c. electron beam
       d. screen

3.4   electron beam

3.5   perpendicular

3.6   electric

1.1 the emission of electrons from a metal surface that is struck by electromagnetic radiation

1.2 The maximum energy of a photo-electron cannot be any greater than the energy of the incident photon minus the energy necessary to escape from the surface.

1.3 Single photons do not have enough energy to be visible.

1.4 The quantum theory is required to give a minimum energy transfer which means that the photon energy can be so low that no electrons are ejected however intense the light.

1.5 photoelectric effect

1.6 a. increases
b. remains constant

1.7 frequency

1.8 quanta

1.9 a. $3 \cdot 10^8 \frac{m}{sec.}$

b. velocity = frequency·wavelength

$\nu = \frac{v}{\lambda} = \frac{3 \cdot 10^8 \frac{m}{sec.}}{6 \cdot 10^{-7} m}$

$\nu = 0.5 \cdot 10^{15}$ H $= 5 \cdot 10^{14}$ H

c. $E = h\nu = (6.63 \cdot 10^{-34}$ joule·seconds$)(5 \cdot 10^{14}$ H$)$
$E = 33.2 \cdot 10^{-20}$ joules

d. $\frac{10 \text{ joules}}{33.2 \cdot 10^{-20} \frac{\text{joules}}{\text{photon}}} = 0.3 \cdot 10^{20}$

photons = $3 \cdot 10^{19}$ photons

1.10 a. $10,000 \frac{\text{joules}}{\text{sec.}}$

b. $E = h\nu = (6.63 \cdot 10^{-34}$ j·sec.$)$ $(8.8 \cdot 10^5$ Hz$)$
$E = 58.3 \cdot 10^{-29} = 5.8 \cdot 10^{-28}$ joules/photon

c. $\frac{10^4 \text{joules}}{5.8 \ 10^{-28} \frac{\text{joules}}{\text{photon}}} = 0.17 \cdot 10^{32}$

photons = $1.7 \cdot 10^{31}$ photons

1.11 a. $v = \nu\lambda$

$\nu = \frac{v}{\lambda} = \frac{3 \cdot 10^8 \frac{m}{sec.}}{5 \cdot 10^{-7} m} = 0.6 \cdot 10^{15}$ Hz
$= 6 \cdot 10^{14}$ Hz

b. $E = h\nu = (6.63 \cdot 10^{-34}$ joule·sec.$)$ $(6 \cdot 10^{14}$ Hz$)$
$E = 39.8 \cdot 10^{-20}$ joules $\approx 4 \cdot 10^{-19}$ joules

c. 1 ev $= 1.6 \cdot 10^{-19}$ joules
$\frac{4 \cdot 10^{-19} \text{ joules}}{1.6 \ 10^{-19} \frac{\text{joules}}{\text{ev}}} = 2.5$ ev

d. energy of incident photon = KE_{max} + energy required to emit photoelectron
2.5 ev $= KE_{max}$ + 2 ev
$KE_{max} = 0.5$ ev

1.12 a. $KE = \frac{1}{2} mv^2$
$= \frac{1}{2}(9.1 \cdot 10^{-31}$ kg$)$ $(7 \cdot 10^5 \frac{m}{sec.})^2$
$KE = 223 \cdot 10^{-21}$ joules $= 2.23 \cdot 10^{-19}$ joules

b. $E = h\nu = (6.63 \cdot 10^{-34}$ joule·sec.$)$ $(8 \cdot 10^{14}$ Hz$)$
$E = 53 \cdot 10^{-20}$ joules $= 5.3 \cdot 10^{-19}$ joules

c. $5.3 \cdot 10^{-19}$ joules $- 2.2 \cdot 10^{-19}$ joules $= 3.1 \cdot 10^{-19}$ joules

1.13 number (density)

1.14 energy (frequency)

1.15 a. $E = h\nu = (6.63 \cdot 10^{-34} \text{ joule} \cdot \text{sec.})$
$(\dfrac{3 \cdot 10^8 \frac{m}{sec.}}{10^{-11} m})$
$E \approx 20 \cdot 10^{-15}$ joules
$E = 2 \cdot 10^{-14}$ joules

b. $\dfrac{(2 \cdot 10^{-14} \text{ joules})}{1.6 \cdot 10^{-19} \frac{joules}{ev}} = 1.25 \; 10^5$ ev

c. incident energy = emitted
energy
$1.25 \cdot 10^5$ ev

d. $1.25 \cdot 10^5$ ev =
(1 electron)$(1.25 \cdot 10^5$ volts)

1.16 $(8 \cdot 10^4 \text{ ev})(1.6 \cdot 10^{-19} \frac{joules}{ev})$
$= 12.8 \cdot 10^{-15}$ joules
$= 1.3 \cdot 10^{-14}$ joules
$E = h\nu$
$\nu = \dfrac{E}{h} = \dfrac{1.3 \cdot 10^{-14} \text{ joules}}{6.63 \cdot 10^{-34} \text{ joule} \cdot \text{sec.}}$
$= 2 \cdot 10^{19}$ Hz

1.17 $(2 \cdot 10^4 \text{ ev})(1.6 \cdot 10^{-19} \frac{joules}{ev})$
$= 3.2 \cdot 10^{-15}$ joules
$E = h\nu = h\dfrac{\nu}{\lambda}$
$\lambda = \dfrac{h\nu}{E} =$
$\dfrac{(6.63 \cdot 10^{-34} \text{ joule} \cdot \text{sec.})(3 \cdot 10^8 \frac{m}{sec.})}{3.2 \; 10^{-15} \text{ joules}}$
$\lambda = 6.2 \cdot 10^{-11}$ m

1.18 $E = h\nu = (6.63 \cdot 10^{-34} \text{ joule} \cdot \text{sec.})$
$(10^{19}$ Hz)
$E = \dfrac{6.6 \cdot 10^{-15} \text{ joules}}{1.6 \cdot 10^{-19} \frac{joules}{ev}} = 4.1 \cdot 10^4$ ev

1.19 a. Planck's constant
b. momentum

1.20 Planck's constant

1.21 $\lambda = \dfrac{h}{mv} =$
$\dfrac{6.63 \cdot 10^{-34} \text{ joule} \cdot \text{sec.}}{(5 \cdot 10^3 \text{ kg})[(8 \cdot 10^4 \frac{m}{hr.})(\frac{1 \text{ hr.}}{3.6 \cdot 10^3 \text{ sec.}})]}$
$\lambda = 0.6 \cdot 10^{-38}$ m $= 6 \cdot 10^{-39}$ m

1.22 $10^7 \frac{m}{sec.} \cdot (m_e = 9.1 \cdot 10^{-31}$ kg)
$\lambda = \dfrac{h}{mv} = \dfrac{6.63 \cdot 10^{-34} \text{ joule} \cdot \text{sec.}}{(9.1 \cdot 10^{-31} \text{ kg})(10^7 \frac{m}{sec.})}$
$\lambda = 0.7 \cdot 10^{-10}$ m $= 7 \cdot 10^{-11}$ m

1.23 $h = \Delta x \cdot \Delta mv$
$\Delta mv = \dfrac{h}{\Delta x} = \dfrac{6.63 \cdot 10^{-34} \text{ joule} \cdot \text{sec.}}{10^{-4} m}$
$\Delta mv = 6.63 \cdot 10^{-30} \dfrac{kg \cdot m}{sec.}$

1.24 a. $h = \Delta x \cdot \Delta mv$
$\Delta v = \dfrac{h}{m\Delta x} = \dfrac{6.63 \cdot 10^{-34} \text{ joule} \cdot \text{sec.}}{(9.1 \cdot 10^{-31} \text{ kg})(10^{-9} \text{ m})}$
$\Delta v = 0.73 \cdot 10^6 \dfrac{m}{sec.} = 7.3 \cdot 10^5 \dfrac{m}{sec.}$

b. $h = \Delta x \cdot \Delta mv$
$\Delta v = \dfrac{h}{m\Delta x} = \dfrac{6.63 \cdot 10^{-34} \text{ joule} \cdot \text{sec.}}{(1.7 \cdot 10^{-27} \text{ kg})(10^{-9} \text{ m})}$
$\Delta v = 3.9 \cdot 10^2 \dfrac{m}{sec.}$

1.25

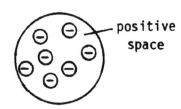

Thompson Model

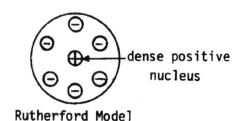

Rutherford Model

1.26   adult check

1.27   the range of wavelengths emitted or absorbed by an object

1.28   the various wavelengths emitted by an excited substance

1.29   the wavelengths that are removed from a continous spectrum when it passes through a substance

1.30   a spectrum containing all wave lengths

1.31   a spectrum that contains only a few discrete wavelengths

1.32

$$\frac{mv^2}{r} = \frac{ke^2}{r^2} \qquad mvr = \frac{nh}{2\pi}$$

$$v^2 = \frac{ke^2 r}{mr^2} \qquad v = \frac{nh}{2\pi mr}$$

$$v = \sqrt{\frac{ke^2}{mr}}$$

$$\sqrt{\frac{ke^2}{mr}} = \frac{nh}{2\pi mr}$$

$$\frac{ke^2}{mr} = \frac{n^2 h^2}{4\pi^2 m^2 r^2}$$

$$r = \frac{n^2 h^2}{4\pi^2 e^2 mk}$$

1.33 $r = n^2 \left(\frac{h^2}{4\pi^2 e^2 mk}\right)$

$$= n^2 \left[\frac{(6.63\cdot10^{-34}\cdot joule\cdot sec)^2}{4(3.14)^2(1.6\cdot10^{-19} coul)^2\cdot}\right.$$
$$\left.\frac{}{(9.1\cdot10^{-31} kg)(9\cdot10^9 \frac{N\cdot m^2}{coul^2})}\right]$$

$r = n^2(0.0053\cdot10^{-8}) = 5.3\cdot10^{-11}$ m

For n = 1, r = $5.3\cdot10^{-11}$ m

For n = 2, r = $2.12\cdot10^{-10}$ m

For n = 3, r = $4.8\cdot10^{-10}$ m

For n = 4, r = $8.5\cdot10^{-10}$ m

For n = 5, r = $1.3\cdot10^{-9}$ m

For n = 6, r = $1.9\cdot10^{-9}$ m

1.34 $\dfrac{5.3\cdot10^{-11} \text{ m}}{1.4\cdot10^{-15} \text{ m}} = 3.8\cdot10^4$

The atomic diameter, then, is 40,000 times larger than its nucleus.

1.35 $(8.65\cdot10^5 \text{ miles})(4\cdot10^4)$
= $3.5\cdot10^{10}$ miles

If the space of the solar system were as empty as the space of a hydrogen atom, the earth would be 35,000,000,000 miles from the sun.

1.36   a.   15

2→1	3→2	4→3	5→4	6→5
3→1	4→2	5→3	6→4	
4→1	5→2	6→3		
5→1	6→2			
6→1				

b. $E = h\nu = h\frac{c}{\lambda}$

$\lambda = \frac{hc}{E}$ (in joules)

$$= \frac{hc}{(1.6\cdot10^{-19} \frac{j}{ev})E(\text{in ev's})}$$

$$\lambda = \left[\frac{(6.63\cdot10^{-34} \text{ joule}\cdot\text{sec.})\cdot}{1.6\cdot10^{-19}\cdot}\right.$$
$$\left.\frac{(3\cdot10^8 \frac{m}{sec.})}{\frac{j}{ev}}\right]\cdot\frac{1}{E*}$$

$\lambda = (1.24\cdot10^{-6} \text{ m}\cdot\text{ev})\frac{1}{E*}$

Transition	*Energy in ev's
2→1	10.2
3→1	12.1
4→1	12.75
5→1	13.06
6→1	13.6
3→2	1.9
4→2	2.55
5→2	2.86
6→2	3.4
4→3	0.65
5→3	0.96
6→3	1.5
5→4	0.31
6→4	0.85
6→5	0.54

1.36   Emitted Wavelengths

0.118×10^{-6} m
0.102×10^{-6} m
0.097×10^{-6} m
0.094×10^{-6} m
0.091×10^{-6} m
0.65×10^{-6} m
0.49×10^{-6} m
0.43×10^{-6} m
0.36×10^{-6} m
1.91×10^{-6} m
1.29×10^{-6} m
0.83×10^{-6} m
4.0×10^{-6} m
1.46×10^{-6} m
2.30×10^{-6} m

1.37 the number of whole electron wave lengths in an electron orbit

1.38 a. circular orbits with balanced forces
      b. orbits quantized: $mvr = n$ times a constant
      c. radiation permitted only during orbit change

1.39 Electrons are excited into higher orbits, then make the transition back to lower energy orbits — emitting light as they do so.

1.40 electrostatic attraction between electron and nucleus must equal the centripital force of the orbiting electron.

1.41 $mvr = \dfrac{nh}{2\pi}$

$v = \dfrac{nh}{2\pi mr}$

$v = \dfrac{(1)(6.63 \cdot 10^{-34} \text{ joule} \cdot \text{sec.})}{2(3.14)(9.1 \cdot 10^{-31} \text{kg})(5.3 \cdot 10^{-11}\text{m})}$

$v = 0.0218 \times 10^8 \dfrac{\text{m}}{\text{sec.}}$

$= 2.18 \times 10^6 \dfrac{\text{m}}{\text{sec.}}$

1.42 $v = \dfrac{nh}{2\pi mr_2}$

$= \dfrac{2(6.63 \cdot 10^{-34} \text{ joule} \cdot \text{sec.})}{2\pi(9.1 \cdot 10^{-31} \text{ kg})(2.12 \cdot 10^{-10} \text{ m})}$

$v = 1.1 \cdot 10^6 \dfrac{\text{m}}{\text{sec.}}$

$t_{rev} = \dfrac{d}{v} = \dfrac{1.33 \ 10^{-9} \text{ m}}{1.1 \cdot 10^6 \ \frac{\text{m}}{\text{sec.}}}$

$= 1.2 \cdot 10^{-15}$ sec.

$\dfrac{10^{-8} \text{ sec.}}{1.2 \cdot 10^{-15} \frac{\text{sec.}}{\text{rev.}}} = 8.3 \cdot 10^6$ revolutions

II. SECTION TWO

2.1 The uncharged particle found in atomic nuclei, it is approximately as heavy as a proton.

2.2 the positively charged particle found in atomic nuclei

2.3 either a proton or a neutron

2.4 1 amu = $1.66 \ 10^{-27}$ kg

$E = mc^2 = (1.66 \cdot 10^{-27} \text{ kg}) \cdot$

$(3 \cdot 10^8 \ \frac{\text{m}}{\text{sec.}})^2$

$E = 1.49 \cdot 10^{-10}$ joules

$\dfrac{1.49 \cdot 10^{-10} \text{ joules}}{1.6 \cdot 10^{-19} \frac{\text{joules}}{\text{ev}}} = 9.313 \ 10^8$ ev

1 amu = 931 Mev

(The accepted value is 1 amu = 931 Mev.)

2.5 The difference between the mass of a nucleus and the mass of the nucleons that it contains is converted into binding energy that holds the nucleus together.

2.6   one of possibly several forms of the nucleus of an element, differing from other forms only in the number of neutrons

2.7   Step 1:

1 proton	=	1.007593 amu
2 neutrons =		
2(1.008982)	= +	2.017964 amu
component mass	=	3.025557 amu
triton mass	= −	3.016448 amu
mass defect	=	0.009109 amu
	=	$9.11 \cdot 10^{-3}$ amu

Step 2:

$(9.11 \cdot 10^{-3}$ amu$)(931 \frac{Mev}{amu}) = 8.5$ Mev

2.8   2.014186 amu + 3.016448 amu $\longrightarrow$
4.003873 + 1.008982 amu + E

mass defect = 0.017779 amu

$(1.78 \cdot 10^{-2}$ amu$)(931 \frac{Mev}{amu}) = 16.6$ Mev

2.9   mass of $_3Li^6$ = 2(4.003873 amu)

$+ (\frac{22.4 \text{ Mev}}{931 \frac{Mev}{amu}}) - (2.014186 \text{ amu})$

mass of $_3Li^6$ = 8.007746 amu

    + 0.024060 amu − 2.014186 amu

mass of $_3Li^6$ = 6.01762 amu

2.10   an unstable nucleus that will decay by emission of radiation

2.11   the time during which half a sample of radioactive material will decay

2.12   At the end of 1 half-life, $\frac{1}{2}$ remains.

At the end of 2 half-lives, $\frac{1}{2} \cdot \frac{1}{2} = \frac{1}{4}$ remains.

At the end of 3 half-lives,

$\frac{1}{2} \cdot \frac{1}{2} \cdot \frac{1}{2} = \frac{1}{8}$ remains.

At the end of 4 half-lives,

$\frac{1}{2} \cdot \frac{1}{2} \cdot \frac{1}{2} \cdot \frac{1}{2} = \frac{1}{16}$ remains.

(4 half-lives)$(1{,}660 \frac{\text{years}}{\text{half-life}})$

= 6,640 years

2.13

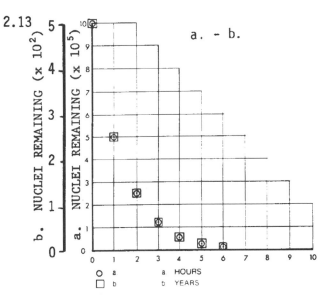

a. – b.

c.   They are identical.

d.   The decay curves for all radioactive substances are identical.

III. SECTION THREE

3.1   Nuclear forces are short-ranged, strong forces that act within the nucleus to hold nucleons together.

3.2   An unstable nucleus vibrates until it produces a dumbbell shape. The two ends repel each other until they separate into two nuclei.

3.3 $_0n^1$

3.4   false

3.5   false

3.6   a.

```
                    |—— Man 3 ——|
        |————————————————|    |—— Man 2 ——|
        |———— Man 1 ————|
    ————————————————————————————————————————
    1600           1700           1800
```

b.   teacher check

3.7   a coulomb force (or) a force between similarly charged objects

3.8   a fission reaction

3.9   a. 4
           b. 1
           c. energy (19.2 mev)

3.10 mass

3.11 $1 \text{ kw} = 1000 \dfrac{j}{\text{sec.}}$

$$\dfrac{1000 \dfrac{j}{\text{sec.}}}{1.6 \times 10^{-19} \dfrac{j}{\text{ev}}} = 6.25 \times 10^{21} \dfrac{\text{ev}}{\text{sec.}}$$

$$= 6.25 \times 10^{15} \dfrac{\text{Mev}}{\text{sec.}}$$

$$\dfrac{6.25 \times 10^{15} \dfrac{\text{Mev}}{\text{sec.}}}{200 \dfrac{\text{Mev}}{\text{fission}}} = 3.13 \times 10^{13} \dfrac{\text{fissions}}{\text{sec.}}$$

3.12 $100 \text{ kw} = 10^5 \dfrac{j}{\text{sec.}} = 6.25 \times 10^{23} \dfrac{\text{ev}}{\text{sec.}}$

$$= \dfrac{6.25 \times 10^{17} \dfrac{\text{Mev}}{\text{sec.}}}{200 \dfrac{\text{Mev}}{\text{fission}}}$$

$$= 3.13 \times 10^{15} \dfrac{\text{fissions}}{\text{sec.}}$$

$$2^n = 3.13 \times 10^{15}$$

$$\therefore n = 52$$

$\text{time} = n \times 10^{-14} \text{ seconds}$
$\qquad = 52 \times 10^{-14} \text{ seconds}$
$\qquad = 5.2 \times 10^{-13} \text{ seconds}$

1.1 a. increased
     b. three

1.2 negative

1.3 a. doubled
     b. negative

1.4 four

1.5 a. increase
     b. two times

1.6 a. shorter
     b. 20

1.7 Then $v = \dfrac{d}{t} = 15$ mph

Now $v = \dfrac{d}{\frac{1}{2}t} = \dfrac{2}{1} = \left(\dfrac{d}{t}\right)$

$= 2(15 \text{ mph})$

$= 30 \text{ mph}$

1.8 Then $v = \dfrac{d}{t} = 30 \dfrac{\text{m}}{\text{sec.}}$

Now $v = \dfrac{\frac{1}{2}d}{t} = \dfrac{1}{2}\left(\dfrac{d}{t}\right)$

$= \dfrac{1}{2}\left(30 \dfrac{\text{m}}{\text{sec.}}\right)$

$= 15 \dfrac{\text{m}}{\text{sec.}}$

1.9 Then $a = \dfrac{v^2}{R} = 20 \dfrac{\text{m}}{\text{sec.}^2}$ (for old $R = 5$m)

Now $a = \dfrac{v^2}{2R} = \dfrac{1}{2}\left(\dfrac{v^2}{R}\right)$ (for new $R = 10$ m)

$a = \dfrac{1}{2}\left(20 \dfrac{\text{m}}{\text{sec.}^2}\right)$

1.10 Then $a = \dfrac{v^2}{R} = 10 \dfrac{\text{m}}{\text{sec.}^2}$

Now $a = \dfrac{(2v)^2}{\frac{1}{2}R} = \dfrac{4}{\frac{1}{2}}\dfrac{v^2}{R}$

$= 8\left(\dfrac{v^2}{R}\right) = 8\left(10 \dfrac{\text{m}}{\text{sec.}^2}\right)$

$a = 80 \dfrac{\text{m}}{\text{sec.}^2}$

1.11 Then $d = \dfrac{1}{2}at^2 = 100$ m

Now $d = \dfrac{1}{2}a(4t^2) = 16\left(\dfrac{1}{2}at^2\right)$

$= 16(100 \text{ m})$

$= 1,600 \text{ m}$

1.12 d

1.13 No force is needed.

1.14 $200 \dfrac{\text{kg} \cdot \text{m}}{\text{sec.}} = mv$

$= (50 \text{ kg})(v)$

$v = \dfrac{200 \dfrac{\text{kg} \cdot \text{m}}{\text{sec.}}}{50 \text{ kg}} = 4 \dfrac{\text{m}}{\text{sec.}}$

1.15 $v = \dfrac{200 \dfrac{\text{kg} \cdot \text{m}}{\text{sec.}}}{100 \text{ kg}} = 2 \dfrac{\text{m}}{\text{sec.}}$

1.16 $m_1 v_1 = m_2 v_2$

$(40 \text{ kg})\left(10 \dfrac{\text{m}}{\text{sec.}}\right) = m_2\left(8 \dfrac{\text{m}}{\text{sec.}}\right)$

$\dfrac{400 \dfrac{\text{kg} \cdot \text{m}}{\text{sec.}}}{8 \dfrac{\text{m}}{\text{sec.}}} = m_2$

$50 \text{ kg} = m_2$

1.17 $F = ma$

        $60\ N = (15\ kg)(a)$

$$a = \frac{60\ N}{15\ kg} = 4\frac{m}{sec.^2}$$

        Resolution of the units:

$$N = \frac{kg \cdot m}{sec.^2}$$

$$\frac{N}{kg} = \frac{\frac{kg \cdot m}{sec.^2}}{kg} = \frac{m}{sec.^2}$$

1.18   a. halved

        b. increased by a factor of 1.5

$$\frac{m_1}{\frac{2}{3}m_1} = \frac{a_2}{a_1} = \frac{-3}{2}$$

        c. doubled

1.19 $F = mg = (3\ kg)(9.8\frac{m}{sec.^2})$

        $F = 29.4\ N$

1.20 $F = m(3g) = 3(mg)$

            $= 3(120\ lbs.) = 360\ lbs$

1.21 $F \propto \frac{1}{d^2} = \frac{1}{(\frac{1}{10})^2} = 100$

        $F = 300\ lbs.$

1.22   b. (Planets sweep out equal
            areas in equal times.)

1.23   b. 5 years

$$\frac{T_A^2}{D_A^3} = \frac{T_B^2}{D_B^3};\ \frac{1^2}{1^3} = \frac{T_B^2}{(3)^3};$$

        $1\ T_B^2 = 27$ years

           $T_B \approx 5$ years

1.24   d

1.25   e

        $E \propto v^2$

1.26   d

1.27   The relative velocity of the
        head-on collision is 60 mph.

1.28   a. They do the same work.

        b. Tow A

1.29   a. Tow A

        b. Tow A

1.30   a   Work $= PE = mgh$

                   $= (5\ kg)(9.8\frac{m}{sec.^2})$

                   $(2\ m)$

                   $= 98\ j$

        b. Efficiency $= \frac{98\ j}{400\ j} \cdot 100\%$

                   $= 24.5\%$

II.   SECTION TWO

2.1   c

2.2   a

2.3   b

2.4   a.   c

        b.   b

        c.   a

        d.   transverse wave

2.5   interference

2.6   interference (or) destructive
        interference

2.7   diffraction (or) interference

2.8   diffraction

2.9   refraction

2.10   toward (toward, away from)

2.11   b

2.12   a

2.13   a

2.14
$$c = f\lambda$$
$$3 \cdot 10^8 \ \frac{m}{sec.} = f(6 \cdot 10^{-7} \ m)$$
$$f = \frac{3 \cdot 10^8 \ \frac{m}{sec.}}{6 \cdot 10^{-7} \ m} =$$
$$0.5 \cdot 10^{15} \ Hz$$
$$f = 5 \cdot 10^{14} \ Hz$$

2.15
$$\frac{H_0}{H_i} = \frac{S_0}{f}$$
$$\frac{4 \ cm}{H_i} = \frac{10 \ cm}{20 \ cm} = \frac{1}{2}$$
$$H_i = 8 \ cm$$

2.16

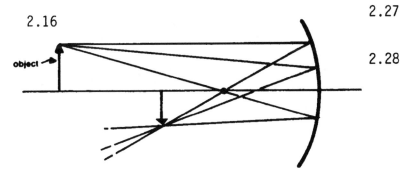

2.17   c

2.18   b

2.19   a

2.20   a

2.21   b

2.22
$$\frac{H_0}{H_i} = \frac{S_0}{f}$$
$$\frac{2 \ in.}{H_i} = \frac{1 \ in.}{20 \ in.} = \frac{1}{20}$$
$$H_i = 40 \ in.$$
The width is also 40 inches, so the image is 40 x 40 inches.

2.23
$$n = \frac{c}{v}$$
$$1.5 = \frac{3 \cdot 10^8 \ \frac{m}{sec.}}{v}$$
$$v = \frac{3 \cdot 10^8 \ \frac{m}{sec.}}{1.5}$$
$$v = 2 \cdot 10^8 \ \frac{m}{sec.}$$

2.24   b

2.25   a

2.26   b or c

2.27   b

2.28
$$v = \frac{d}{t} = 330 \ \frac{m}{sec.}$$
$$330 \ \frac{m}{sec.} = \frac{d}{\frac{1}{2} \ sec.}$$
$$d = 165 \ m$$
This distance is the length down and back. The length of the corridor = $\frac{1}{2} d = 82\frac{1}{2}$ m.

III.   SECTION THREE

3.1   (Hans Christian) Oersted

3.2   field

3.3   a. magnetic
      b. electric

3.4   a magnetic field (and an electric field)

3.5   deficiency of electrons

3.6   the discovery of the electron

3.7   electrons

3.8   free electrons

151

3.9 The outer electrons of some elements are easily separated from their atoms; these elements, principally metals, are good conductors.

3.10 Orbiting electrons generate tiny magnetic fields. The atoms of iron can be oriented to make the many small magnetic fields cumulative.

3.11 Any order:
a. a "yes-no" character
b. exert force
c. attract and repel

3.12 Either order:
a. charges can exist alone; poles occur in pairs
b. a charge will attract any uncharged object; a pole will attract certain substances only

3.13 a sphere of influence

3.14 surface

3.15 newtons per coulomb

3.16 (Charles) Coulomb

3.17 Ampere

3.18 a. potential difference
b. distance

3.19 concentric with

3.20 perpendicular to

3.21

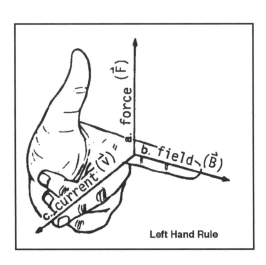

Left Hand Rule

3.22 a single north-seeking pole of "unit" strength

3.23 An object (a piece of iron) in a magnetic field experiences a force. The practical outer limit of a field is the distance from the pole beyond which an object does not respond to the force.

3.24 Any actual charged object, even an electron, has mass that is in-fluenced by gravity, friction, and extraneous electric fields. The effect of an electric field can be "measured" accurately only by an ideal unit positive charge, a hypothetical model.

3.25 A test charge, which is positive by definition, would travel along one such vector if released in the field.

3.26 gravity

3.27 Similar charges seek to be the maximum distance possible from each other, which guarantees that they will be evenly spaced on the surface.

3.28 The field changes direction 120 times per second, which is too fast for the mass of the compass needle to respond.

3.29 Only when the secondary coil is actively being cut by magnetic field lines building outward from, or collapsing toward, the primary coil is a current pro-duced in this coil.

3.30 The magnetic force is exerted on the moving charges in the wire.

3.31 The current must have some component perpendicular to the field.

3.32 free electrons

3.33   current

3.34   circuit

3.35   a.   positive
       b.   negative

3.36   induction

3.37   greater

3.38   series

3.39   conservation of charge

3.40   emf (or) generator (or) battery

3.41   resistance

3.42   potential drop (or) voltage drop

3.43   a.   emf
       b.   resistance

3.44   a.   length
       b.   cross-section area

3.45   resistivity

3.46   less

3.47   emf

3.48   a.   current
       b.   potential

3.49   Outer electrons of metals are
       loosely held and can easily be
       freed to flow as a current.

3.50   **Either order:**
       a.   batteries
       b.   generators

3.51 $R = \rho \frac{l}{A}$

3.52   Any order:
       a.   seat of emf
       b.   conductor
       c.   resistance

3.53 $E = V_{R_1} + V_{R_2} = 2V_{R_1}$
       $V_{R_1} = \frac{1}{2}E = \frac{1}{2}(12 \text{ v}) = 6 \text{ v}$

3.54 $E = V_{R_1} = V_{R_2}$
       $V_{R_2} = E = 12 \text{ v}$

3.55   a. $P = \frac{V^2}{R}$
       b. $P = I^2 R$
       c. $P = IV$

3.56   a. $P = IV$
       $I = \frac{P}{V} = \frac{60 \text{ watts}}{120 \text{ volts}} = 0.5 \text{ amps}$
       b. $P = \frac{\text{energy}}{\text{time}}$
       energy $= Pt = (60 \text{ watts})$
       $(24 \text{ hrs.} \cdot \frac{3600 \text{ sec.}}{\text{hr.}})$
       energy $= 5.2 \cdot 10^6$ joules
       (t must be expressed in seconds.)

IV.   SECTION FOUR

4.1   John Dalton

4.2   Rutherford

4.3   a stream of electrons from a
       filament (cathode)

4.4   the measurement of the electron's
       charge--the fundamental
       electrical charge

4.5   The atom was divisible.

4.6   They revealed that the mass of
       an atom is concentrated in a
       small region called a nucleus.

4.7   Thomson discovered the electron
       and measured its charge-to-mass
       ratio.

4.8   false

4.9   false

4.10   true

4.11   true

4.12   true

4.13 $E = h\nu$

4.14   Hertz noticed that light caused
       certain metals to emit electrons
       if the frequency of the light
       was adequate. If the frequency
       were inadequate, no amount of
       intensity could cause emission.

4.15   The discrete distance an
       electron will jump.

4.16   Upon the frequency of its
       radiation.

4.17   Incandescent solids emit
       continuous spectra, some of
       which are in the visible range,
       incandescent gases emit bright-
       line spectra of discrete wave
       lengths.

4.18   Radiation begins above 0°K
       (-273° C).

4.19   Bright lines in its emmision
       spectrum have the same wave-
       lengths as the dark lines of
       its absorption spectrum.

4.20   A subincandescent gas absorbs
       specific wavelengths from the
       radiation emitted by some other
       incandescent source.

4.21   Each line represents a discrete
       frequency emitted by the atoms
       of the gas.

4.22   Energy from incident photons
       (quanta of radiation) is
       transferred to the electrons.

4.23   A metal will begin to emit
       electrons when the frequency
       of the incident radiation is
       higher than the threshold
       frequency for the metal.

4.24   The work function of a particular
       metal is the energy required to
       free an electron from the metal.
       The work function is related to
       the threshold frequency by the
       equation $E = h\nu$.

4.25   Planck's Constant

4.26   wavelength

4.27   electron-volt

4.28   a.   6563; $4.57 \cdot 10^{14}$; $3.03 \cdot 10^{-19}$;
            1.9; $n = 3$ to $n = 2$

       Given $\lambda = 6563\,\overset{\circ}{A} = 6563 \times 10^{-10}$ m

       $\nu = \dfrac{c}{\lambda} = \dfrac{3 \times 10^8\,\frac{m}{sec.}}{6563 \times 10^{-10}\,m} = 4.57 \times 10^{14}\,Hz$

       $E = h\nu = (6.63 \times 10^{-34}\,j\text{-}sec.) \cdot (4.57 \times 10^{14}\,Hz)$
       $= 3.03 \times 10^{-19}$ joules

       $E(\text{in ev's}) = \dfrac{3.03 \times 10^{-19}\,j}{1.6 \times 10^{-19}\,\frac{j}{ev}} = 1.9$ ev

       From ENERGY LEVELS FOR HYDROGEN
       (p. 48), an emission of 1.9 represents
       an electron moving from $n = 3$
       to $n = 2$.

       b.   4861; $6.17 \cdot 10^{14}$; $4.09 \cdot 10^{-19}$;
            2.56; $n = 4$ to $n = 2$
       c.   4340; $6.91 \cdot 10^{14}$; $4.58 \cdot 10^{-19}$;
            2.86; $n = 5$ to $n = 2$
       d.   4101; $7.32 \cdot 10^{14}$; $4.85 \cdot 10^{-19}$;
            3.03; $n = \infty$ to $n = 2$

4.29   a. $E = (13.6\ ev)(1.6 \cdot 10^{-19}\,\frac{j}{ev})$
            $= 2.18 \cdot 10^{-18}$ j

       $\nu = \dfrac{E}{h} = \dfrac{2.18 \cdot 10^{-18}\,j}{6.63 \cdot 10^{-34}\,j\text{-}sec.}$
       $= 3.29 \cdot 10^{15}\,Hz$

       $\lambda = \dfrac{c}{\nu} = \dfrac{3 \cdot 10^8\,\frac{m}{sec.}}{3.29 \cdot 10^{15}\,Hz} = 912\,\overset{\circ}{A}$

       b.   no
       c.   ultraviolet
       d.   Ultraviolet radiation can
            ionize hydrogen from the
            body's molecules, causing
            undesirable chemical
            reactions.
       e.   Hydrogen's emission spectrum
            shows only visible lines;
            many of hydrogen's emissions
            are outside the visible
            range at both ends.

4.30   Each line represents a jump
       between discrete energy levels
       available to the electron(s)
       of the gas in question.

4.31   X rays penetrated a half inch of aluminum.

4.32   The object must be nearly the size of atoms or smaller.

4.33   Roentgen observed flashes on a flourescent screen when high-energy electrons impacted on an anode in a cathode-ray tube.

4.34   DeBroglie's equation implies that every moving object has an associated wavelength.

4.35   The momentum and/or position of an atom-sized particle is changed by any technique used to measure it.

4.36 $\Delta x \cdot \Delta mv \approx h$
Δx is the displacement, and Δmv is the change in momentum, of any subatomic particle subjected to observational radiation. The symbol h is Planck's Constant.

4.37   Newtonian physics describes the interactions of force and matter for a statistically large number of atoms acting as a single subject. Atomic physics describes the interactions of individual atoms and their components.

4.38 $\lambda = \dfrac{h}{mv} = \dfrac{6.63 \; 10^{-34} \text{ j-sec.}}{(2 \cdot 10^{-2} \text{ kg})(10^2 \frac{m}{\text{sec.}})}$
$\lambda = 3.32 \cdot 10^{-34} \text{ m} = 3.32 \cdot 10^{-24} \text{ Å}$

4.39 $\lambda = \dfrac{h}{mv} =$
$\dfrac{6.63 \cdot 10^{-34} \text{ j-sec.}}{(9.1 \cdot 10^{-31} \text{ kg})(10^{-2} \cdot 3 \cdot 10^8 \frac{m}{\text{sec.}})}$
$\lambda = 2.43 \cdot 10^{-10} \text{ m} = 2.43 \text{ Å}$

4.40   a neutron

4.41   protons

4.42   protons plus neutrons (or) nucleons

4.43   103

4.44   a. mass number
b. atomic number

4.45   isotopes

4.46   three

4.47   deuterium

4.48   tritium

4.49   a deuteron

4.50   a triton

4.51   less than

4.52   atomic mass unit (amu)

4.53   Positively-charged protons tend to repel each other; the binding energy is stronger and holds them together.

4.54   The sum of a nucleus's components' masses is greater than the mass of the nucleus.

4.55   2(2.014186 amu) = 3.015779 amu + 1.008982 + E
4.028372 amu = 4.024761 amu + E
mass defect = 0.003611 amu
E = (0.003611 amu) (931 $\frac{Mev}{amu}$) = 3.36 Mev

4.56   All radioactive elements, whatever the original mass, decay to half that original mass in a fixed time (its half-life), which is a function of the element only.

4.57 $\dfrac{22,800 \text{ years}}{5700 \frac{\text{years}}{\text{half-life}}}$ = 4 half-lives

$\dfrac{1}{2} \cdot \dfrac{1}{2} \cdot \dfrac{1}{2} \cdot \dfrac{1}{2} = \dfrac{1}{16}$ original sample

4.58   Isotopes have identical numbers of protons, but different numbers of neutrons.

4.59   a.   1 proton   = 1.007593 amu

2 neutron at
   1.008982   = +2.017964 amu
                    3.025557 amu

1 triton   = -3.016448 amu
mass defect   0.009109 amu

b.   (0.009109 amu)(931 $\frac{Mev}{amu}$) =
     8.48 Mev

4.60   a.   1
       b.   2
       c.   3
       d.   tritium

1.01 e

1.02 c

1.03 h

1.04 i

1.05 f

1.06 k

1.07 j

1.08 b

1.09 g

1.010 a

1.011

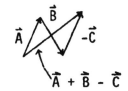

$\vec{A} + \vec{B} - \vec{C}$

1.012

1.013 $(4.2)(4.0) \times 10^{5-9}$
16.8×10^{-4}
1.68×10^{-3}

1.014 $\dfrac{6.0}{3.0} \times 10^{-6-3}$
2.0×10^{-9}

1.015 30 km

1.016 2000 mg (or 2×10^{3}mg)

1.017 200,000 cm (or 2×10^{5}cm)

1.018 1 ms

1.019 6 km

1.020 .035 mg (or 3.5×10^{-2}mg)

SELF TEST 2

2.01 h

2.02 g

2.03 b

2.04 d

2.05 e

2.06 j

2.07 i

2.08 c

2.09 k

2.010 a

2.011 2000 mm

2.012 0.035 km

2.013 11 miles

2.014

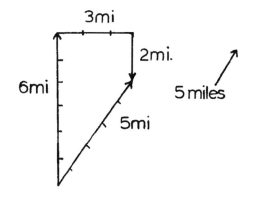

2.015 D = m/v   {Dimensions}
     v = m/D   {g cm³/ gm}
     $v = \dfrac{7.5\ g}{2.5\ g/cm^3}$
     v = 3.0 cm³

2.016 ⟵————————⟶ ; 0 units

2.017 v = Area X height
     v = (3.6 cm²)(2.0 cm)
     v = 7.2 cm³

2.018 $(3.2 \times 10^{-4})(4.02)$
     $(3.2)(4.02) \times 10^{-4}$
     12.86×10^{-4} (round off permitted)
     1.29×10^{-3}

2.019 $\dfrac{3 \times 10^2}{5 \times 10^{-4}} = 3/5 \times 10^{2(-4)}$
     $.6 \times 10^6 = 6 \times 10^5$

2.020 70 miles

SELF TEST 3

3.01 e

3.02 l

3.03 f

3.04 n

3.05 g

3.06 k

3.07 m

3.08 o

3.09 j

3.010 c

3.011 5 miles

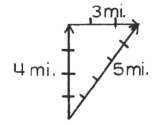

3.012 $\vec{v} = \dfrac{\Delta \vec{d}}{\Delta t}$
     $= \dfrac{5\ miles}{\frac14\ hr}$ ↗
     20 mph ↗

3.013 $\dfrac{8.1 \times 10^{-3}}{3 \times 10^2}$
     $\dfrac{8.1 \times 10^{-3-2}}{3}$
     2.7×10^{-5}

3.014 11 units

3.015 $D = \dfrac{m}{v} = \dfrac{45\ g}{\frac14(60\ cm^3)}$
     $= \dfrac{45\ g}{15\ cm^3}$
     $= 3\ \dfrac{g}{cm^3}$

3.016 20 mph for ½ hr = 10 miles
     40 mph for 1 hr = 40 miles
     30 mph for ½ hr = 15 miles
     50 mph for 2 hr = 100 miles
                     165 miles

3.017 S avg = $\dfrac{\text{total distance}}{\text{total time}}$
     $= \dfrac{(10 + 40 + 15 + 100)\ miles}{(\frac12 + 1 + \frac12 + 2)hr}$
     $= \dfrac{165\ miles}{4\ hr} = 41\frac14$ mph

3.018 Since a marble will roll down a pan and up the other side just as high (if there is no friction); then if you extend the bottom of the pan so that it extends infinitely out, the marble will keep on rolling.

3.019 To express very large numbers or very small numbers without having to use lots of zeros.

158

3.020 A pilot of an airplane needs to know which way the wind is blowing or he'll get blown off course.

SELF TEST 4

4.01   j

4.02   a

4.03   d

4.04   b

4.05   f

4.06   o

4.07   n

4.08   k

4.09   i

4.010 g

4.011 $d = \frac{1}{2} gt^2$
$= \frac{1}{2}(-32 \text{ ft/s}^2)(5s)^2$
$= -(\frac{1}{2})(32)(25) \text{ ft}$
$d = -400 \text{ ft, down}$

4.012 $v^2 = v_0^2 + 2a\ d$ $= 0$
$(20 \text{ m/s})^2 = 0 + 2(a)(50m)$
$\frac{400 \text{ m}^2/\text{s}^2}{100 \text{ m}} = a$ $= 0$

$\vec{a} = 4 \text{ m/s}^2$

4.013 $\vec{v} = \frac{\Delta \vec{d}}{\Delta t} = \frac{400 \text{ miles}}{10 \text{ hr}}, \text{ east}$
$= 40 \text{ mph, east}$

4.014 $d = \frac{1}{2} at^2$ $d_o = 0; v_o = 0$

$441 \text{ m} = \frac{1}{2}(5)(9.8 \text{ m/s}^2)\ t^2$
$\frac{441 \text{ m}}{24.5 \text{ m/s}^2} = t^2$

(remember to take the square root)

$\sqrt{18s^2} = t$
$4.24s = t$

4.015 $a = v^2/R$
$= \frac{(10 \text{ mph})^2}{.2 \text{ mi}}$
$= \frac{100 \text{ mi}^2/\text{hr}^2}{.2 \text{ mi}} = 500 \text{ mi/hr}^2$
$a = 500 \text{ mi/hr}^2$

4.016 $\frac{2 \times 10^{-3}}{2.5 \times 10^4} = \frac{2}{2.5} \times 10^{-3-(4)}$
$= 0.8 \times 10^{-7}$
$= 8 \times 10^{-8}$

4.017 10 units NE,

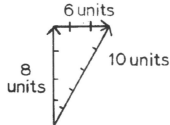

4.018 $\vec{a} = \frac{\Delta \vec{v}}{\Delta t}$

it points to the center at all times

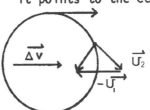

4.019 Because the force of gravity causes a body to speed up while falling at 9.8 m/s² or 32 ft/s²

4.020 a. an object speeding up in a straight line
b. an object slowing down in a straight line
c. an object at the same speed going in an arc of a circle

4.021 $\vec{v} = \Delta d/\Delta t$
$\vec{a} = \Delta v/\Delta t$

SELF TEST 5

5.01   b

5.02   j

5.03   a

5.04   e

5.05   d

5.06   g

5.07   k

5.08   i

5.09   c

5.010   h

5.011 $\vec{a} = \dfrac{\Delta \vec{v}}{\Delta t} = \dfrac{\vec{v}\ final - \vec{v}\ initial}{\Delta t}$

$\qquad = \dfrac{10\ m/s - 20\ m/s}{5\ s}$

$\qquad = \dfrac{-10\ m/s}{5\ s}$

$\qquad = -2\ m/s^2$, a negative acceleration

5.012   35 mph x 1 hr = 35 miles;   1 hr
$\qquad$ 40 mph x ½ hr = 20 miles;   ½ hr
$\qquad$ 50 mph x 2 hr = $\underline{100\ miles}$; $\underline{2\ hr}$
$\qquad\qquad\qquad\qquad$ 155 miles   3½ hr
$\qquad$ speed = $\dfrac{\Delta d}{\Delta t} = \dfrac{155\ miles}{3.5\ hr}$
$\qquad$ speed = 44.3 mph

5.013 $\vec{D}$ = 11.7 units   N.E.

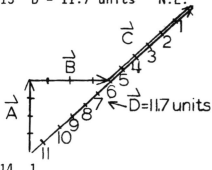

5.014   1

5.015 3.2×10^5 cm

5.016   Mass and time; they do not depend on direction

5.017   An object at rest stays at rest or an object in motion stays in motion unless there are unbalanced external forces acting on it.

5.018   Because at every point in a region of space there is a value for temperature as recorded on a thermometer.

5.019   A resultant occurs by combining (add or subtract) two or more vectors and a component occurs when you take one vector and split it into its horizontal and vertical vectors.

5.020   Example:
Molecules like tiny B-B's moving rapidly around and colliding with each other.

SCIENCE 1202

SELF TEST 1

1.01   c

1.02   a

1.03   f

1.04   g

1.05   d

1.06   b

1.07 $F\Delta t = mv$

$\qquad v = \dfrac{F\Delta t}{m}$

$\qquad\quad = \dfrac{(2000\ N)(0.3\ s)}{0.1\ kg}$

$\qquad v = 6000\ \dfrac{m}{s}$

1.08 mv = momentum

$\qquad\quad = (2000\ kg)(60\ \dfrac{m}{s})$

$\qquad\quad = 120{,}000\ \dfrac{kg \cdot m}{s}$

$\qquad$ or $1.2 \cdot 10^5\ \dfrac{kg \cdot m}{s}$

1.09 $F\Delta t = mv$; $F = \frac{mv}{\Delta t}$

$F = \frac{120,000 \frac{kgm}{s}}{.05 \ s}$

$F = 2.4 \cdot 10^6 \ N$

1.010 Impulse = $F\Delta t$

= $(2.4 \cdot 10^6 \ N)(0.05 \ s)$

= $1.2 \cdot 10^5 \ N \cdot s$ {$N \cdot s = \frac{Kg \cdot m}{s}$}

1.011 $F = ma$ $m = \frac{F}{a}$

$m = \frac{6 \ N}{2 \ \frac{m}{s^2}} = 3 \ kg$

$m = m_{cart} + m_{rock}$

$m_{rock} = 3 \ kg - 1 \ kg$

$m_{rock} = 2 \ kg$

1.012 $F = ma$

= $(4 \ kg)(3 \ \frac{m}{s^2})$

$F = 12 \ N$

$F' = m'a'$ $12 \ N = (2 \ kg)(a)$

$a = 6 \ \frac{m}{sec^2}$

1.013 Because $mv = F\Delta t$, the answer to 1.08 should equal the answer to 1.010.

1.014 An object in motion will stay in motion if no forces are exerted on it.

1.015 The object would accelerate toward the planet.

1.016 Momentum is mass times velocity. When the first car hits the second, it exerts a force over a period of time, which is the impulse.

SELF TEST 2

2.01   a
2.02   i
2.03   h
2.04   e
2.05   f
2.06   b
2.07   d
2.08   g
2.09   j
2.010 c

2.011 $d = \frac{1}{2} gt^2$; $t^2 = \frac{2d}{g}$

$t = \sqrt{\frac{2d}{g}}$

$t = \sqrt{\frac{2(250 \ ft)}{5 \ \frac{ft}{s^2}}} = 10 \ sec$

2.012 $F_{5R} = \frac{1}{(5R)^2} F$

= $\frac{1}{25}$ (weight)

= $\frac{1}{25}$ (100 lbs)

= 4 lbs

2.013 $v = -gt$

$v = -(9.8 \ \frac{m}{s^2})(4 \ s)$

$v = 39 \ \frac{m}{s}$

2.014 impulse = $F\Delta t = mg\Delta t$

= $(1 \ kg)(9.8 \ \frac{m}{s^2})(0.1 \ s)$

impulse = $0.98 \ \frac{kg \cdot m}{s}$

= 0.98 N·s

2.015 momentum = mv

$$mv = (0.1 \text{ kg})(2000 \frac{m}{s})$$

$$= 200 \frac{kg \cdot m}{s}$$
or
$$mv = (100 \text{ kg})(3 \frac{m}{s})$$

$$= 300 \frac{kg \cdot m}{s}$$
greater momentum

2.016 $g_{moon} = \frac{1}{6} g_{earth} = \frac{1}{6}(9.8 \frac{m}{s^2})$

$$g_m = 1.63 \frac{m}{s^2}$$

a_g at 3r $= (\frac{1}{3}r)^2 g_m = \frac{1}{9}(1.63 \frac{m}{s^2})$

$$a_g = 0.18 \frac{m}{s^2}$$

2.017 a. no
b. The answer is the same because FΔt = mv (the impulse equals the momentum of the object).

2.018 The inertial and gravitational masses, although measured by two different methods, are equal to each other.

2.019 because our sun and planets all have a gravitational force field that exerts an attractive force on the object

2.020 a. yes
b. Because although r is small to make F as large as possible, the value of G is so small $(6.67 \cdot 10^{-11} \frac{N \cdot m}{kg^2})$ that F is small.

SELF TEST 3

3.01 f

3.02 c

3.03 j

3.04 a

3.05 h

3.06 b

3.07 k

3.08 i

3.09 g

3.010 e

3.011 $F = m (\frac{4\pi^2 R}{T^2})$
$$= \frac{0.1 \text{ kg}(4)(3.14)^2(.5 \text{ m})}{(1 \text{ s})^2}$$
$$F = 1.97 \text{ N}$$

3.012 Impulse = FΔt = mv

$$= (2000 \text{ kg})(60 \frac{m}{s})$$

$$= 1.2 \times 10^5 \frac{kg \cdot m}{s} \text{ (or N} \cdot \text{s)}$$

3.013 $F = ma; \quad a = \frac{F}{m}$

$$a = \frac{12 \text{ N}}{3 \text{ kg}}$$

$$= 4 \frac{m}{s^2}$$

3.014 12.6 s

$$a = \frac{2\pi v}{T} \qquad T = \frac{2\pi v}{a}$$

$$T = \frac{2(3.14)(40 \frac{m}{s})}{20 \frac{m}{s^2}}$$

$$T = 12.6 \text{ s}$$

3.015 F = ma

$$F = m \frac{\Delta v}{\Delta t}$$

$$F\Delta t = m(\frac{\Delta v}{\Delta t}) \Delta t$$

$$F\Delta t = m\Delta v$$

3.016 $d = v_0 t - \frac{1}{2} g t^2$

$d = (-10 \frac{m}{s})(2 \text{ s}) - \frac{1}{2}(9.8 \frac{m}{s^2})(2 \text{ s})^2$

$d = -20 \text{ m} - 19.6 \text{ m}$

$= -39.6 \text{ m}$

falls 39.6 m so was thrown from that height

3.017 Gravitational mass is found by measuring its weight in the earth's gravitational field $(m_g = \frac{F}{g})$. Inertial mass is measured by exerting a known force on it and measuring its acceleration $(m_i = \frac{F}{a})$.

3.018 because a value exists at every point in space as measured by a test mass

3.019 $a = \frac{\Delta v}{\Delta t}$, and the Δv points toward the center. $F = ma$; and, since a points towards the center, so also does F (a centerward pull exists on an object that is swinging in a circle).

3.020 because $F = \frac{G m_1 m_2}{R^2}$ and $F \propto \frac{1}{R^2}$; because the force is inversely proportional to R^2--an inverse square law

SELF TEST 4

4.01 d

4.02 k

4.03 b

4.04 g

4.05 e

4.06 c

4.07 i

4.08 j

4.09 f

4.010 h

4.011 $m_1 \vec{v}_{1i} = m_1 \vec{v}_{1f} + m_1 \vec{v}_{2f}$

$m_1 = m_2$

$\vec{v}_{1i} = \vec{v}_{1f} + \vec{v}_{if}$

$= 2.8 \frac{m}{s}$

at a 45° angle

$2.8 \frac{m}{sec}$ NE

4.012 $m_1 v_{1i} = (m_1 + m_2)v_f$

$(.4 \text{ kg})v_{1i} = (.4 \text{ kg} + .4 \text{ kg})(8 \frac{m}{s})$

$v_{1i} = 16 \frac{m}{s}$

4.013 $F_{action} = F_{reaction} = 12 \text{ lbs}$

4.014 4R from center of earth

$F \propto \frac{1}{r^2}; = \frac{1}{4^2} = \frac{1}{16}$

$F = \frac{1}{16}(320 \text{ lbs}) = 20 \text{ lbs}$

4.015 Reaction force is the ball hitting the bat with a force of 5 N.

4.016 $v = v_0 - gt$

$0 = 64 \frac{ft}{s} - (32 \frac{ft}{s^2})(t)$

$t = \frac{64 \frac{ft}{s}}{32 \frac{ft}{s}} = 2 \text{ s}$

4.017 The action and reaction force act on different objects; therefore, the net force is not zero.

4.018 Yes, F is proportional to the mass and acceleration (F = ma) anywhere; however, the acceleration due to gravity will be less than on the moon.

4.019 From Newton's third law, F_{action} = $F_{reaction}$ Since times are the same, $m_1v_1 = m_2v_2$.

4.020 Mass does not change for an object when you change its location; however, weight can change since it depends on the force of attraction of another object.

SELF TEST 5

5.01 c

5.02 i

5.03 d

5.04 f

5.05 h

5.06 k

5.07 a

5.08 b

5.09 e

5.010 j

5.011
$$\frac{R_e^3}{T_e^2} = \frac{R_x^3}{T_x^2}$$
$$\frac{(1 \ au)^3}{(1 \ year)^2} = \frac{(4 \ au)^3}{T_x^2}$$
$$T_x = 8 \ years$$

5.012 A_1A_2 requires twice as much time as B_1B_2.

5.013 mass does not change
$$w = m(\tfrac{1}{2} g)$$
$$= 4 \ kg(4.9 \ \tfrac{m}{s^2})$$
$$w = 19.6 \ N$$

5.014 $F = \dfrac{mv^2}{R}$

$= \dfrac{(2 \ kg)(3 \ \tfrac{m}{s})^2}{0.5 \ m}$ = 36 N

5.015 $(1000 \ kg)(66 \ \tfrac{m}{s}) = (3000 \ kg)(v)$
$$v = \frac{66,000}{3,000}$$
$$v = 22 \ \tfrac{m}{s}$$

5.016 $v = \dfrac{d}{t}$

$d = vt = (1000 \ \tfrac{ft}{s})(0.5 \ s)$

d = 500 ft. (time to fall = time

of travel)

5.017 Neither is totally correct. The Copernican system correctly places the sun at the center, but incorrectly attributes circular orbits to the planets.

5.018 the Coperinican system; the sun at the center of planets traveling in circular orbits

5.019 Newton discovered the Law of Universal Gravitation: $F = \dfrac{Gm_1m_2}{R^2}$.

5.020 The intensity decreases as the inverse square of the distance. That is, at 2 d, the intensity = $\tfrac{1}{4}$; and at 3 d it is $\tfrac{1}{9}$, and so on.

1.01   c

1.02   f

1.03   g

1.04   h

1.05   a

1.06   j

1.07   k

1.08   d

1.09   e

1.010   i

1.011   b

1.012   c

1.013   b

1.014   b

1.015   c

1.016   a

1.017   b

1.018   c

1.019   c

1.020   b

1.021 $m = 10\ g = 0.010\ kg$

$KE = \frac{1}{2}mv^2$

$= (\frac{1}{2})(.01kg)(300\ \frac{m}{sec.})^2$

$= 450\ \frac{kg \cdot m^2}{sec.^2}$

$= 450\ J$

1.022 $v_2 = 3v_1$

$v_2{}^2 = 9v_1{}^2$

$KE = \frac{1}{2}mv^2$

$KE_2 = 9\ KE_1$

1.023 $PE = mgh$

$= (60\ kg)(9.8\ \frac{m}{sec.^2})(10\ m)$

$= 5,880\ J$

1.024 $Fd = work$

$(300\ N)d = 12,000\ J$

$d = \frac{12,000\ J}{300\ m}$

$d = 40\ m$

1.025   All have the same potential energy. All started from the same height and reached the same height. Since work = Fd = mgh, all did the same work.

1.026   Force is the product of mass and acceleration. The acceleration due to gravity would be the same for all objects but the masses could differ. The larger the mass the greater the force, the "harder the fall".

SELF TEST 2

2.01   a

2.02   j

2.03   h

2.04   b

2.05   g

2.06   k

2.07   i

2.08   c

2.09   e

2.010   f

2.011 at 100% efficiency IMA = AMA

$$MA = \frac{500 \text{ lb.}}{50 \text{ lb.}}$$

$$MA = 10$$

2.012 $MA = 6 = \dfrac{D_E}{D_R}$

$$6 = \frac{D_E}{2 \text{ in.}}$$

$$D_E = 12 \text{ in.}$$

2.013 $KE = \frac{1}{2}mv^2 = (\frac{1}{2})(5 \text{ kg})(10 \frac{m}{sec.})^2$

$$= 250 \text{ J}$$

$$PE = mgh$$

$$= (5 \text{ kg})(9.8 \frac{m}{sec.^2})(5 \text{ m})$$

$$= 245 \text{ J}$$

$$KE = PE + loss$$

$$loss = 250 \text{ J} - 245 \text{ J}$$

$$= 5 \text{ J}$$

2.014 $P = \dfrac{\Delta E}{\Delta t} = \dfrac{\Delta (Fd)}{\Delta t}$

$$= \frac{(100 \text{ N})(5 \text{ m})}{4 \text{ sec.}}$$

$$= 125 \text{ watts}$$

2.015 $PE = mgh$

$$= (60 \text{ kg})(9.8 \frac{m}{sec.^2})(10 \text{ m})$$

$$= 5,880 \text{ J}$$

2.016 $Fd = \frac{1}{2}mv^2$

$$(25 \text{ N})(4 \text{ m}) = \frac{1}{2}(2 \text{ kg})v^2$$

$$v^2 = \frac{100 \text{ N} \cdot m}{1 \text{ kg}}$$

$$v^2 = 100 \frac{m^2}{sec.^2}$$

$$v = 10 \frac{m}{sec.}$$

2.017 Although very little force may be used, the distance over which the effort takes place increases and work = force times distance.

2.018 With M.A. of 2 an effort of 1,000 lb. is needed which is impractical. With a 2,000,00 M.A. then $\frac{1}{1000}$ lb. only is needed, but to move it 1 inch the effort must be moved 2,000,000 inches, also impractical.

2.019 a. Work output is less than energy input.
b. Frictional losses account for this difference.

2.020 potential energy of water stored behind a dam, to kinetic energy of falling water, to mechanical energy of the turbines, to electrical energy through the wires, to light energy in the bulb

SELF TEST 3

3.01 f

3.02 g

3.03 d

3.04 c

3.05 h

3.06 a

3.07 j

3.08 k

3.09 i

3.010 b

3.011 n

3.012 m

3.013 l

3.014 o

3.015 p

3.016 efficiency = $\dfrac{T_h - T_c}{T_h} \cdot 100\%$

$= \dfrac{800°K - 600°K}{800°K} \cdot 100\%$

$= \dfrac{200°K}{800°K} \cdot 100\%$

efficiency = 25%

3.017 total energy = KE + heat
20,000 J = 5,000 J + heat
heat = 15,000 J

3.018 a. PE = $\frac{3}{4}$PE$_{max}$

$= \frac{3}{4}$(16 J)

PE = 12 J

b. total energy = KE + PE
16 J = KE + 12 J
KE = 4 J

3.019 KE = $\frac{1}{2}mv^2$

$= \frac{1}{2}$(4 kg)(16 $\frac{m}{sec.}$)^2

= 512 J

3.020 a. M.A. = $\dfrac{500\ lb.}{10\ lb.}$

= 50

b. M.A. = 50 = $\dfrac{d}{3\ in.}$

d = 150 in.

3.021 A heat engine transforms heat energy into mechanical energy. The earth receives heat from the sun and transforms it into mechanical energy to evaporate water and produce winds.

3.022 heat loss = heat gain
(m)(C)(Δt) = (m)(C)(Δt)
(50 g)(0.2)(50°C) = (m)(1)(10°C)

$m = \dfrac{(50\ g)(0.2)(50°C)}{10°C}$

= 50 g

3.023 heat = (m)(L$_v$)

= (100 kg)(93 $\frac{kcal}{kg}$)

= 9,300 kcal

3.024 Whenever energy is transformed from one form to another, some energy is transformed into heat energy and is unusable.

3.025 Engine fuel temperature has an upper limit for safety; excessive temperatures can damage the engine; exhaust gases are substantially above absolute zero.

3.026 Force is a push or pull, energy is the ability to do work, and power is an energy rating with respect to time.

1.01   a

1.02   c

1.03   b

1.04   f

1.05   e

1.06   crest

1.07   trough

1.08   wavelength

1.09   amplitude

1.010   equilibrium position

1.011   a. $T = 0.5$ sec.

b. $f = \frac{1}{T} = 2$ Hz

c. $v = \frac{d}{t} = \frac{20 \text{ cm}}{0.5 \text{ sec.}} = 40 \frac{\text{cm}}{\text{sec.}}$

d. $v = f\lambda$
$\lambda = \frac{v}{f} = \frac{40 \frac{\text{cm}}{\text{sec.}}}{2 \text{ Hz}} = 20$ cm

1.012   a. $f = \frac{15 \text{ pulses}}{3 \text{ sec.}} = 5$ Hz

b. $T = \frac{1}{f} = \frac{1}{5}$ sec.

c. $\lambda = \frac{45 \text{ cm}}{15 \text{ pulses}} = 3$ cm

d. $v = f \cdot \lambda = (5 \text{ Hz})(3 \text{ cm}) = 15 \frac{\text{cm}}{\text{sec.}}$

$v = \frac{d}{t} = \frac{45 \text{ cm}}{3 \text{ sec.}} = 15 \frac{\text{cm}}{\text{sec.}}$

1.013   amplitude = 0.25 cm

1.014   The crest is the highest point of the wave; the amplitude is the height of the crest measured from equilibrium.

2.01   nodes

2.02   antinodes

2.03   destructive

2.04   standing

2.05   frequency

2.06   diffraction

2.07   refraction

2.08   interference

2.09   decreases

2.010   inverted

2.011   d

2.012   b

2.013   c

2.014   b

2.015   c

2.016   a

2.017   b

2.018   d

2.019   a

2.020   c

2.021   Diffraction is observed when a wave passes through an opening that is smaller than the wavelength.

2.022

student work

168

2.023 $v = f\lambda$

$\lambda = \dfrac{v}{f} = \dfrac{3 \cdot 10^8 \text{ m/sec.}}{9 \cdot 10^5 \text{ Hz}}$

$(900 \text{ KHz} = 9 \cdot 10^5 \text{ Hz})$

$= 333 \text{ m}$

2.024

SELF TEST 3

3.01 beats

3.02 resonance

3.03 Doppler effect

3.04 shorter

3.05 shock waves

3.06 temperature

3.07 total internal reflection

3.08 (periodic) wave

3.09 period

3.010 longitudinal

3.011 refraction

3.012 smaller

3.013 rarefaction

3.014 constructive

3.015 amplitude (height)

3.016

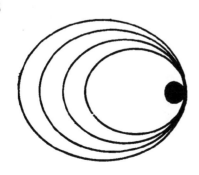

3.017

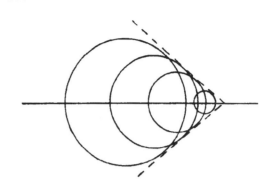

3.018 $v = \dfrac{d}{t}$

$d = vt$

$= (330 \, \dfrac{\text{m}}{\text{sec.}})(2 \text{ sec.})$

$d = 660 \text{ m}$ (down and back)

$\dfrac{1}{2}d = 330 \text{ m}$

3.019 a. $\dfrac{1}{2}\lambda = L_2 - L_1$

$= 2.25 \text{ m} - .75 \text{ m}$

$= 1.5 \text{ m}$

$\lambda = 3 \text{ m}$

b. $v = (330 + .6 \text{ T}) \, \dfrac{\text{m}}{\text{sec.}}$

$= 330 + (.6)(25) \, \dfrac{\text{m}}{\text{sec.}}$

$= 330 + 15 \, \dfrac{\text{m}}{\text{sec.}}$

$= 345 \, \dfrac{\text{m}}{\text{sec.}}$

c. $v = f\lambda$

$f = \dfrac{v}{\lambda}$

$f = \dfrac{345 \, \frac{\text{m}}{\text{sec.}}}{3 \text{ m}}$

$= 115 \text{ Hz}$

3.020 a. $v = f\lambda$

$\lambda = \dfrac{v}{f} = \dfrac{330 \, \frac{\text{m}}{\text{sec.}}}{990 \text{ Hz}}$

$= \dfrac{1}{3} \text{ m}$

b. $T = \dfrac{1}{f} = \dfrac{1}{990 \text{ Hz}} = \dfrac{1}{990} \text{ sec.}$

3.021 1563 Hz − 1560 Hz = 3 Hz = 3 beats

1.01   k

1.02   f

1.03   e

1.04   c

1.05   g

1.06   d

1.07   a

1.08   b

1.09   i

1.010   j

1.011   Galileo

1.012   Olaus Roemer

1.013   Albert Michelson

1.014   Measured from the normal, the angle of reflection = 25°.

1.015 $n = \dfrac{c}{v}$

$\quad = \dfrac{3 \cdot 10^8 \ \frac{m}{sec.}}{2 \cdot 10^8 \ \frac{m}{sec.}}$

$n = 1.5$

1.016   angle of incidence = angle of reflection
$\quad\quad 50° = 50°$

1.017 $n = \dfrac{c}{v}$

$v = \dfrac{c}{n} = \dfrac{3 \cdot 10^8 \ \frac{m}{sec.}}{1.33}$

$v = 2.25 \cdot 10^8 \ \frac{m}{sec.}$

1.018   because light causes the electrons to vibrate, analogous to sound affecting tuning forks, and the vibrating electrons scatter light

1.019   because with two polarized disks perpendicular to each other only transverse waves would be stopped

1.020   Light is made of colors of varying frequencies and each frequency has a different index of refraction and bends at a different angle.

1.021   Roemer timed the rotation of several of the moons of Jupiter when the earth was close and far from Jupiter. The orbit of Earth divided by the time difference was his measure of the speed of light.

1.022   Michelson reflected light from an 8-sided mirror to a plane mirror and back to the 8-sided mirror.

SELF TEST 2

2.01   b

2.02   e

2.03   h

2.04   j

2.05   a

2.06   d

2.07   f

2.08   c

2.09   k

2.010   g

2.011   a. $S_i S_o = f^2$

$S_i = \dfrac{f^2}{S_o}$

$= \dfrac{(10 \text{ cm})^2}{5 \text{ cm}}$

$= \dfrac{100}{5} \text{ cm}$

$S_i = 20 \text{ cm}$

b. $\dfrac{H_o}{H_i} = \dfrac{S_o}{f}$

$\dfrac{3 \text{ cm}}{H_i} = \dfrac{5 \text{ cm}}{10 \text{ cm}}$

$H_i = \dfrac{(3 \text{ cm})(10 \text{ cm})}{5 \text{ cm}}$

$H_i = 6 \text{ cm}$

2.012 $n = \dfrac{c}{v}$

$v = \dfrac{c}{n}$

$v = \dfrac{3 \cdot 10^8 \ \frac{m}{sec.}}{1.7}$

$v = 1.8 \cdot 10^8 \ \dfrac{m}{sec.}$

2.013

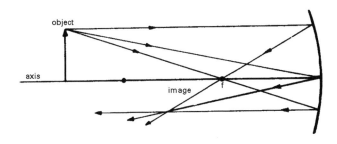

2.014

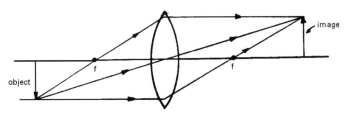

2.015 $n = \dfrac{sin \ i}{sin \ r}$

$sin \ r = \dfrac{sin \ i}{n} = \dfrac{0.15}{1.5}$

$sin \ r = 0.10$

2.016   Polarization demonstrates the transverse wave nature of light.

2.017   Each color has its own index of refraction. Glass refracts violet more than blue, blue more than green, and so on.

2.018   The focal point is a point on the axis through which incident rays parallel to the axis will reflect.

2.019   **In dispersive media waves of high frequency refract more than do waves of low frequency.**

2.020   Roemer did not know the accurate diameter of the earth's orbit.

SELF TEST 3

3.01   a

3.02   e

3.03   j

3.04   k

3.05   c

3.06   d

3.07   h

3.08   i

3.09   f

3.010   b

3.011 $n = \dfrac{c}{v}$

$= \dfrac{3 \cdot 10^8 \ \frac{m}{sec.}}{2 \cdot 10^8 \ \frac{m}{sec.}}$

$n = 1.5$

3.012

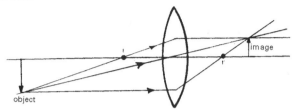

3.013   real, diminished, inverted

3.014

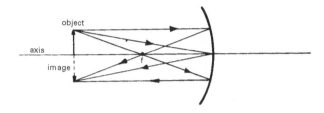

3.015   real, inverted image the same
size as the object

3.016   The image is virtual, erect, and
diminished.

3.017 $n = \dfrac{sin\ i}{sin\ r} = \dfrac{0.2173}{0.1738} = 1.25$

3.018   Metallic plates emit electrons
only when light of a certain
minimum frequency shines on
them. The frequency, therefore,
must determine the energy of the
light.

3.019   Taylor's experiment showed that
even individual photons have
wave characteristics, as
evidenced by the diffraction
pattern.

3.020   Light passing from a low-velocity
medium to a high-velocity medium
at an incident angle larger than
the critical angle will be
totally reflected.

3.021   As light passes from A to B, the
ray bends towards the normal in
medium B.

3.022   When transmitted into a high-
velocity medium, light refracts
away from the normal; particles
refract toward the normal.

1.01   b

1.02   a

1.03   b

1.04   b

1.05   a

1.06   b

1.07   d

1.08   c

1.09   b

1.010   b

1.011   electroscope

1.012   charges

1.013   a. charges
       b. force between

1.014   a. repel
       b. attract

1.015   increases

1.016   push or pull

1.017   result of an excess of electrons

1.018   result of a deficit of electrons

1.019   object with abundant free electrons

1.020   object with few free electrons

1.021   The wand contains relatively few electrons and the discharge is rapid; the battery produces an abundance of charges and the discharge is prolonged.

2.01   field

2.02   unit positive

2.03   Coulomb's

2.04   lightning

2.05   vertical

2.06   currents

2.07   William Gilbert

2.08   excess

2.09   free

2.010   increases

2.011

2.012

2.013 $F_1 \propto \dfrac{1}{d^2}$, $F_2 \propto \dfrac{1}{(2d_1)^2}$

$$\frac{F_2}{F_1} = \frac{\frac{1}{(2d_1)^2}}{\frac{1}{(d_1)^2}} = \frac{d_1^2}{(2d_1)^2} = \frac{d_1^2}{4d_1^2} = \frac{1}{4}$$

$$F_2 = \frac{F_1}{4} = \frac{4\ N}{4}$$

$$F_2 = 1\ N$$

173

2.014 $E = \dfrac{F}{q} = \dfrac{2\ N}{2\ coul} = 1\dfrac{N}{coul}$

2.015   Outer electrons of elements in good conductors are loosely held and are able to migrate readily.

SELF TEST 3

3.01   capacitor

3.02   potential

3.03   increases

3.04   remains the same

3.05   charges

3.06   conductor

3.07   current

3.08   ampere

3.09   conservation of charge

3.010   field

3.011   false

3.012   true

3.013   true

3.014   true

3.015   false

3.016 $E = \dfrac{v}{d} = \dfrac{12\ v}{0.5\ cm} = 24\ \dfrac{v}{cm}$

3.017 $E = \dfrac{F}{q} = \dfrac{5\ N}{0.3\ coul} = 16.7\ \dfrac{N}{coul}$

3.018
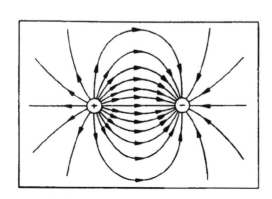

3.019 $F_1 \propto \dfrac{1}{d_1{}^2}$, $F_2 \propto \dfrac{1}{(2d_1)^2}$

$\dfrac{F_2}{F_1} = \dfrac{\dfrac{1}{4d_1{}^2}}{\dfrac{1}{d_1{}^2}} = \dfrac{d_1{}^2}{4d_1{}^2} = \dfrac{1}{4}$

$F_2 = \dfrac{F_1}{4} = \dfrac{16\ N}{4} = 4\ N$

3.020   **unit positive**

3.021   **lightning**

3.022   insulator

3.023   positive

3.024   free

3.025   A region of space in which a test charge experiences a force is a field.

3.026   Any material possessing loosely held electrons that are free and capable of movements is a conductor.

1.01   positive

1.02   electromotive force

1.03   electrolyte

1.04   chemical

1.05   mechanical

1.06   **elevation or height (potential)**

1.07   potential

1.08   conductance

1.09   directly

1.010   potential

1.011   b

1.012   b

1.013   c

1.014   a

1.015   d

1.016 $G = \sigma\frac{A}{l}$

$G = (0.9 \text{ unit } - \text{ cm}^{-1})(\frac{3 \text{ cm}^2}{14 \text{ cm}})$

$G = 0.2 \text{ units}$

1.017 $G = \sigma\frac{A}{l}$

$\sigma = \frac{Gl}{A} = \frac{(0.08 \text{ units})(20 \text{ cm})}{0.4 \text{ cm}^2}$

$\sigma = 4 \text{ unit } - \text{ cm}^{-1}$

2.01   conductance

2.02   cross-sectional area

2.03   ohm

2.04   ohm-cm

2.05   a. length
        b. resistivity

2.06   resistivity

2.07   salt

2.08   semiconductors

2.09   drops or decreases

2.010   potential

2.011   false

2.012   false

2.013   true

2.014   true

2.015   false

2.016 $R = \rho\frac{l}{A} = (1.8 \cdot 10^{-6} \text{ ohm } - \text{ cm})$

$\frac{90 \text{ cm}}{0.02 \text{ cm}^2}$

$R = 8.1 \cdot 10^{-3} \text{ ohms}$

2.017 $G = \frac{1}{R} = \frac{1}{4.0 \cdot 10^{-4} \text{ ohms}}$

$= 2.5 \cdot 10^3 \text{ mhos}$

2.018 $G = \sigma\frac{A}{l}$

$\sigma = \frac{Gl}{A} = \frac{(3.5 \cdot 10^3 \text{ mhos})(2 \text{ cm})}{0.06 \text{ cm}^2}$

$\sigma = 116.7 \cdot 10^3 \text{ mho-cm}^{-1}$
$= 1.167 \cdot 10^5 \text{ mho-cm}^{-1}$

3.01   current

3.02   Ohm's

3.03   series

3.04   branches

3.05   ammeter

3.06   voltmeter

3.07   decrease

3.08   remain constant

3.09   decreases

3.010 volt

3.011 resistor

3.012 electrical

3.013 silver or copper

3.014 higher

3.015 c

3.016 a

3.017 b

3.018 d

3.019 a

3.020 c

3.021 $I = \dfrac{E}{R} = \dfrac{12 \text{ volts}}{4 \text{ ohms}} = 3 \text{ amps}$

3.022 $R_T = 3\Omega + 4\Omega + 5\Omega = 12\Omega$

3.023 $\dfrac{1}{R_T} = \dfrac{1}{2\Omega} + \dfrac{1}{3\Omega} + \dfrac{1}{4\Omega} = \dfrac{6}{12\Omega}$

$+ \dfrac{4}{12\Omega} + \dfrac{3}{12\Omega}$

$\dfrac{1}{R_T} = \dfrac{13}{12\Omega}$

$R_T = \dfrac{12}{13}\ \Omega$

3.024 $P = I^2R = (2 \text{ amps})^2(6\Omega)$

$= 24 \text{ watts}$

3.025 $P = \dfrac{E^2}{R} = \dfrac{(12\ V)^2}{6\Omega} = \dfrac{144\ V^2}{6\Omega}$

$= 24 \text{ watts}$

3.026 $R = \rho\dfrac{l}{A} = (1.8 \cdot 10^{-6} \text{ ohm-cm})\dfrac{270 \text{ cm}}{0.03 \text{ cm}^2}$

$R = 1.6 \cdot 10^{-2}\Omega$

1.01   true

1.02   true

1.03   false

1.04   true

1.05   true

1.06   true

1.07   false

1.08   true

1.09   false

1.010 false

1.011 a

1.012 b

1.013 b

1.014 c

1.015 a

1.016

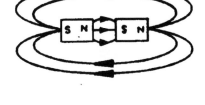

1.017

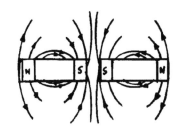

SELF TEST 2

2.01   a. Henry
       b. Faraday

2.02   electric currents

2.03   magnetic field

2.04   inversely

2.05   current

2.06   work or energy

2.07   a. area
       b. magnetic field

2.08   induction

2.09   parallel

2.010 the center of the earth

2.011 b

2.012 d

2.013 b

2.014 a

2.015 a

2.016 c

2.017 d

2.018 b

2.019 c

2.020 c

2.021 work = charge•potential
       work = 25 coul•12 V
       work = 300 joules

3.01   true

3.02   true

3.03   true

3.04   false

3.05   true

3.06   false

3.07   true

3.08   false

3.09   true

3.010 false

3.011 a

3.012 d

3.013 a

3.014 b

3.015 d

3.016 b

3.017 a

3.018 b

3.019 a

3.020 d

3.021

3.022

3.023   Force

3.024   work = charge•potential
        potential = $\dfrac{\text{work}}{\text{charge}}$
        $V = \dfrac{3 \text{ joules}}{6 \text{ coulombs}} = 0.5$ volts

178

1.01 a

1.02 c

1.03 e

1.04 g

1.05 b

1.06 d

1.07 f

1.08 h

1.09 j

1.010 k

1.011 frequency or energy

1.012 remove the electron from the metal

1.013 intensity

1.014 frequency

1.015 ground

1.016 a. h or Planck's constant
      b. frequency of the photon

1.017 a. **Planck's constant or h**
      b. momentum

1.018 diffraction or interference

1.019 de Broglie wave lengths

1.020 a

1.021 b

1.022 b

1.023 a

1.024 b

1.025 d

1.026 c

1.027 c

1.028

$$v = \frac{nh}{mr\,2\pi}$$

$$= \frac{9 \times 6.63 \times 10^{-34}}{(9.1 \times 10^{-31})(\frac{85.9}{2} \times 10^{-10})(2)(3.14)}$$

$$= 2.43 \times 10^5 \ \frac{m}{sec.}$$

$$C = \pi d = (3.14)(85.9 \times 10^{-10} \ m)$$
$$= 2.7 \times 10^{-8} \ m$$

$$f = \frac{1}{period} = \frac{1}{\frac{C}{v}} = \frac{1}{\frac{2.7 \times 10^{-8} \ m}{2.43 \times 10^5 \ \frac{m}{sec.}}}$$

$$= \frac{1}{1.13 \times 10^{-13} \ sec.}$$
$$= 9 \times 10^{12} \ Hz$$

1.029

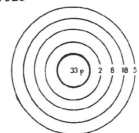

SELF TEST 2

2.01 d

2.02 f

2.03 h

2.04 j

2.05 b

2.06 c

2.07 e

2.08 g

2.09 i

2.010 k

2.011 nucleons

2.012 Either order:
    a. neutrons
    b. energy

2.013 Either order:
    a. line
    b. continuous

2.014 **nucleus (center)**

2.015 alpha particles or helium nuclei

2.016 d

2.017 b

2.018 a

2.019 b

2.020 c

2.021 d

2.022 a

2.023 Pass the radiant energy
through a gas. Specific wavelengths of the radiation are
absorbed by the atoms and cause
the electrons to jump to higher
energy levels. The wavelengths
absorbed produce the line spectrum.

2.024

$$mvr = \frac{nh}{2\pi}$$

$$v = \frac{nh}{2\pi mr}$$

$$= \frac{5 \times 6.63 \times 10^{-34}}{(2)(3.14)(9.1 \times 10^{-31})(1.33 \times 10^{-9})}$$

$$= 4.4 \times 10^5 \ \frac{m}{sec.}$$

SELF TEST 3

3.01 e

3.02 g

3.03 i

3.04 k

3.05 c

3.06 b

3.07 a

3.08 f

3.09 d

3.010 j

3.011 Pass the light through a filter
such as a piece of colored glass.

3.012
$$d = 1.06 \qquad d_{15} = (15)^2 C^1$$
$$r = n^2 C \qquad\qquad = (15)^2 (1.06 \ \overset{\circ}{A})$$
$$d = n^2 C^1 \qquad\qquad = 238.5 \ \overset{\circ}{A}$$
$$d_1 = 1^2 C^1 \qquad\qquad = 239 \ \overset{\circ}{A}$$
$$C^1 = \frac{d_1}{1^2}$$
$$= 1.06 \ \overset{\circ}{A}$$

3.013

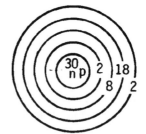

The most abundant isotope
of zinc has 34 neutrons.

3.014 The resultant nuclei in both
reactions have less mass than
the initial reactants. This
mass loss is converted to an
energy equivalent.

3.015

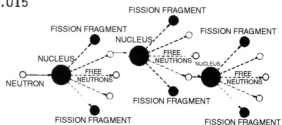

3.016   nucleus

3.017   a. higher
         b. lower
         c. lower
         d. higher

3.018   mass

3.019   the mass discrepency or mass
         defect

3.020   a. atomic
         b. mass

3.021   He nucleus emitted by a nucleus

3.022   electron emitted by nucleus

3.023   electromagnetic radiation emitted
         by nucleus

1.01 a

1.02 k

1.03 e

1.04 c

1.05 i

1.06 g

1.07 h

1.08 d

1.09 f

1.010 j

1.011 b

1.012 c

1.013 c

1.014 a

1.015 c

1.016 efficiency $= \dfrac{1000 \text{ J}}{3000 \text{ J}}$ 100%

efficiency $= 33\frac{1}{3}\%$

1.017 $\dfrac{T_A{}^2}{R_A{}^3} = \dfrac{T_B{}^2}{R_B{}^3}$; $\dfrac{1^2}{1^3} = \dfrac{T_B{}^2}{4^3}$;

$T_B{}^2 = 64$

$T_B = 8$ years

1.018 $KE = \frac{1}{2} mv^2 = \frac{1}{2}(100 \text{ kg}) (20 \frac{m}{\text{sec.}})^2$

$KE = 20,000$ J

1.019 Weight $= m(\frac{1}{6})(g) = (24 \text{ kg})(\frac{1}{6})$

$(9.8 \frac{m}{\text{sec.}^2})$

Weight $= 39.2$ N
(Allow 3 points for the answer
left correctly in terms of g;
i. e., 4gN.)

1.020 $m_1 v_1 = m_2 v_2$

$(0.5 \text{ kg})(8 \frac{m}{\text{sec.}}) = (2 \text{ kg})(v_2)$

$v_2 = \dfrac{4\frac{\text{kg} \cdot m}{\text{sec.}}}{2 \text{ kg}}$

$v_2 = 2 \frac{m}{\text{sec.}}$

SELF TEST 2

2.01 **a**

2.02 **d**

2.03 **e**

2.04 g

2.05 i

2.06 k

2.07 b

2.08 j

2.09 h

2.010 c

2.011 c

2.012 d

2.013 a

2.014 a

2.015 a

2.016 **c**

2.017 b

2.018 c

2.019 c

2.020 a

2.021 $F = ma$

20 N $= m(4 \frac{m}{sec.})$

$m = \dfrac{20 \text{ N}}{4 \frac{m}{sec.^2}}$

$= 5 \text{ kg}$

2.022 $33\% = \dfrac{E_{out}}{6000 \text{ J}} \cdot 100\%$

$\dfrac{33}{100} = \dfrac{E_{out}}{6000 \text{ J}}$

$\dfrac{E_{out}}{6000 \text{ J}} = \dfrac{1}{3}$

$E_{out} = 2000 \text{ J}$

2.023 $S_0 S_i = f^2$

$(2 \text{ cm})(S_i) = (30 \text{ cm})^2$

$2S_i = 900 \text{ cm}$

$S_i = 450 \text{ cm}$

2.024 $n = \dfrac{c}{v}$

$1.33 = \dfrac{3 \cdot 10^8 \frac{m}{sec.}}{v}$

$v = \dfrac{3 \cdot 10^8 \frac{m}{sec.}}{1.33}$

$v = 2.25 \cdot 10^8 \frac{m}{sec.}$

2.025 $v = f\lambda$

$330 \frac{m}{sec.} = (990 \text{ } Hz)\lambda$

$\lambda = \dfrac{330 \frac{m}{sec.}}{990 \text{ } Hz}$

$\lambda = \dfrac{1}{3} \text{ m}$

2.026

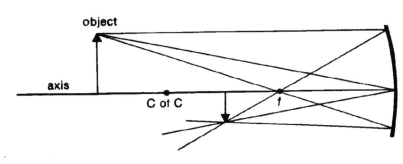

SELF TEST 3

3.01   j

3.02   f

3.03   a

3.04   k

3.05   i

3.06   c

3.07   b

3.08   d

3.09   g

3.010   h

3.011   c

3.012   d

3.013   d

3.014   a

3.015   c

3.016   d

3.017   d

3.018 b

3.019 b

3.020 a

3.021 d

2.022 b

3.023 b

3.024 d

3.025 d

3.026 c

3.027 b

3.028 b

3.029 a

3.030 c

3.031 a

3.032 c

3.033 c

3.034 a

3.035 d

3.036 acceleration

3.037 Kepler

3.038 weight

3.039 efficiency

3.040 power

3.041 centripetal acceleration or force

3.042 longitudinal

3.043 transverse

3.044 interference (diffraction or polarization)

3.045 refraction

3.046 Either order:
    a. crests
    b. troughs

3.047 frequency

3.048 wavelength

3.049 interference

3.050 a. magnetic field $(\vec{B})$
    b. force $(\vec{F})$
    c. current $(\vec{i})$ or $(\vec{v})$

3.051 $E = V_{R_1} = V_{R_2}$

$V_{R_1} = E = 24 \text{ v}$

3.052 $E = V_{R_1} + V_{R_2} = 2V_{R_1}$

$V_{R_1} = \frac{1}{2}E = \frac{1}{2}(6\ V) = 3 \text{ v}$

3.053 a. $P = IV$

$I = \frac{P}{V} = \frac{60 \text{ watts}}{120 \text{ volts}} = 0.5 \text{ amps}$

    b. $P = \frac{\text{energy}}{\text{time}}$

energy = Pt = (60 watts)

$(24 \text{ hrs.} \cdot \frac{3600 \text{ sec.}}{\text{hr.}})$

energy = $5.2 \cdot 10^6$ joules

(t must be expressed in seconds.)

SELF TEST 4

4.01 d

4.02 g

4.03 k

4.04 h

4.05 j

4.06 i

4.07 b

4.08 f

4.09   c

4.010 a

4.011 g

4.012 c

4.013 b

4.014 e

4.015 h

4.016 f

4.017 a

4.018 d

4.019 k

4.020 j

4.021 a

4.022 c

4.023 b

4.024 b

4.025 b

4.026 b

4.027 c

4.028 a

4.029 d

4.030 a

4.031 velocity

4.032 Kepler

4.033 weight

4.034 $9.8 \frac{m}{sec.^2}$ or $\frac{32ft.}{sec.^2}$

4.035 efficiency

4.036 work

4.037 power

4.038 centripetal

4.039 momentum

4.040 Newton

4.041 work

4.042 acceleration

4.043 velocity

4.044 refracts

4.045 longitudinal

4.046 John Dalton

4.047 charge of an electron (fundamental charge)

4.048 atomic nucleus

4.049 planetary

4.050 cathode

4.051 electron

4.052 nucleons

4.053 protons

4.054 three

4.055 hydrogen

4.056 energy

4.057 binding energy

4.058 frequency

4.059 photoelectric effect

4.060 electromagnetic

4.061 X rays

4.062 **wavelength**

4.063 Either order:
   a. momentum
   b. location

4.064 146

4.065 neutron

4.066 three

4.067 momentum = $m \cdot v$ = $(0.3 \text{ kg})(10 \frac{\text{m}}{\text{sec.}})$

momentum = $3 \frac{\text{kg-m}}{\text{sec.}}$

4.068 F_1 = 360 lbs.

$$F_2 = G \frac{m_1 m_2}{(3r)^2}$$

$$360 = G \frac{m_1 m_2}{r^2}$$

$$F_2 = \frac{360 r^2}{9 r^2}$$

$$= 40 \text{ lbs.}$$

4.069 $\dfrac{a_2 = \dfrac{(2v)^2}{r}}{a_1 = \dfrac{v^2}{r}} = \dfrac{4}{1}$

The acceleration is quadrupled.

4.070 efficiency = $\frac{150 \text{ J}}{200 \text{ J}} \cdot 100\%$

efficiency = 75%

4.071 $KE = \frac{1}{2} m v^2 = \frac{1}{2}(40 \text{ kg})(10 \frac{\text{m}}{\text{sec.}})^2$

$KE = 2,000$ J

4.072 $F = mg = (60 \text{ kg})(9.8 \frac{\text{m}}{\text{sec.}^2})$

$F = 588$ N

4.073 $\nu = \frac{c}{\lambda} = \frac{3 \cdot 10^8 \frac{\text{m}}{\text{sec.}}}{6.8 \cdot 10^{-7} \text{ m}} = 4.4 \cdot 10^{14} \text{ Hz}$

4.074 a.

1 proton	=	1.007593 amu
1 neutron	=	+ 1.008982 amu
		2.016575 amu
1 deuteron	=	- 2.014186 amu
mass defect	=	0.002389 amu

   b. $(0.002389 \text{ amu})(931 \frac{\text{Mev}}{\text{amu}})$ =
      2.22 Mev

4.075 ΔE = (-1.5 ev) - (-3.4 ev)

E = $(1.9 \text{ ev})(1.6 \times 10^{-19} \frac{\text{j}}{\text{ev}})$

$= 3.04 \times 10^{-19}$ j

$E = h\nu = h\frac{c}{\lambda}$

$\lambda = h\frac{c}{E}$ = $(6.63 \cdot 10^{-34} \text{ j-sec.})$

$\left(\dfrac{3 \cdot 10^8 \frac{\text{m}}{\text{sec.}}}{3.04 \cdot 10^{-19} \text{ j}} \right)$

$\lambda = 6.543 \cdot 10^{-7}$ m = 6543 Å

4.076 From the graph at 1½ half-lives 35% of the original parent nuclei remain. Therefore, 65% of the sample must be fission fragments.

100%	original parent nuclei
- 35%	parent nuclei remaining
65%	fission fragments

65% (5 grams) = 3.25 g

Full credit for a reasonably approximate answer.

TEST

KEYS

1. b

2. d

3. f

4. e

5. c

6. a

7. a. 3×10^8 m/s
    b. 3×10^5 km/s
    c. $3.2 \ 10^7$ s
    d. Ly = distance = speed $\times$ time
       $= (3 \times 10^8$ m/s$)(3.2 \times 10^7$ s$)$
       $= 9.6 \times 10^{15}$ m
    e. $(9.6 \times 10^{15}) \times 10^2$ cm =
       9.6×10^{17} cm

8. $\vec{v} = \dfrac{\vec{\Delta d}}{\Delta t} = \dfrac{80 \text{ miles, east}}{2 \text{ hrs}}$

    $v = 40$ mph, east (a vector)

9. $D = \dfrac{\text{Mass}}{\text{Volume}} = 40 \text{ g/cm}^3 = \dfrac{40 \text{ g}}{1 \text{ cm}^3}$

    $D \text{ new} = \dfrac{40 \text{ g}}{1/3 \text{ cm}^3} = 40 \times 3 \text{ g/cm}^3$

    $D = 120 \text{ g/cm}^3$

10. Can't calculate displacement because no directions are given.
    Distance = 7 miles
    2 + 3 + 2 = 7 miles
    distance = 7 miles

11.
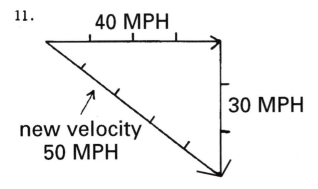

40 MPH

30 MPH

new velocity
50 MPH

12. v^2 final = v^2 initial + 2a(d final
    - d initial)
    $0^2 = (30 \text{ m/s})^2 + 2a(350 \text{ m} - 200 \text{ m})$
    $\dfrac{-900 \text{ m}^2/\text{s}^2}{2 (150 \text{ m})} = \dfrac{-900}{300} \text{ m/s}^2 = -3 \text{ m/s}^2 = a$
    or
    $v = v_0 + at$
    $0 = 30 \text{ m/s} + a(10\text{s})$
    $\dfrac{-30}{10\text{s}} \text{ m/s} = a = -3 \text{ m/s}^2$

13. Using a barometer measure the pressure at various altitudes and draw a relationship between altitude and pressure (a sharp student will note that this will differ over the equator as compared to the polar regions.)

14. Concentric circles simplify the picture for the young child but it is not completely accurate in describing the solar system it is merely an approximation or a simplification.

1. f

2. a

3. d

4. e

5. g

6. b

7. d

8. b

9. c

10. a

11.
$$\frac{R_E^3}{T_E^2} = \frac{R_p^3}{T_p^2}$$

$$\frac{(1 \text{ Au})^3}{(1 \text{ year})^2} = \frac{R_p^3}{(8 \text{ year})^2}$$

$$R_p^3 = 64 \text{ (Au)}$$

$$R_p = 4 \text{ Au}$$

12. $F = \frac{mv^2}{R} = \frac{(20 \text{ kg})(10 \frac{m}{s})^2}{15 \text{ m}}$

$F = 133.3 \text{ N}$

13.

14. $F\Delta t = mv, \quad \Delta t = \frac{mv}{F}$

$\Delta t = \frac{(2000 \text{ kg})(40 \frac{m}{s})}{4 \times 10^5 \text{ N}}$

$\Delta t = 0.20 \text{ sec}$

15. $m_1 v_1 = (m_1 + m_2)v$

$(10,000 \text{ kg})(30 \frac{m}{s}) =$

$(10,000 \text{ kg} + 20,000 \text{ kg})v$

$3 \cdot 10^5 \frac{kg \cdot m}{s} = 3 \cdot 10^4 \text{ kg} \cdot v$

$v = 10 \frac{m}{s}$

16. $d = \frac{1}{2} at^2$

$78.4 \text{ m} = \frac{1}{2}(9.8 \frac{m}{s^2})t^2$

$t^2 = \frac{(78.4 \text{ m})(2)}{9.8 \frac{m}{s^2}} = 16 \text{ s}^2$

$t = 4 \text{ s}$

1. a
2. b
3. k
4. d
5. h
6. g
7. f
8. i
9. j
10. c

11. total energy = KE + PE

$E = \frac{1}{2}mv^2 + mgh$

$= \frac{1}{2}(2\ kg)(10\ \frac{m}{sec.})^2 +$

$(2\ kg)(9.8\ \frac{m}{sec.^2})(50\ m)$

$= \frac{1}{2}(2\ kg)(100\ \frac{m^2}{sec.^2}) +$

$(100\ kg \cdot m)(9.8\ \frac{m}{sec.^2})$

$E = 100\ kg \cdot \frac{m^2}{sec.^2} + 980\ kg \cdot \frac{m^2}{sec.^2}$

$= 1,080\ J$

12. PE = KE

$mgh = \frac{1}{2}mv^2$

$(5\ sl)(32\ \frac{ft.}{sec.^2})(100\ ft) = \frac{1}{2}(5\ sl)(v^2)$

$v^2 = 2(3,200)\frac{ft.^2}{sec.^2} = 6,400\ \frac{ft.^2}{sec.^2}$

$v = 80\ \frac{ft.}{sec.}$

13. $P = \frac{E}{t} = \frac{mgh}{t}$

$= \frac{(500\ kg)(9.8\ \frac{m}{sec.^2})(20\ m)}{10\ sec.}$

$P = \frac{98,000\ kg \cdot \frac{m^2}{sec.^2}}{10\ sec.} = 9,800\ \frac{J}{sec.}$

$= 9,800\ watts$

14. $IMA = \frac{30\ ft.}{2\ ft.} = 15$

$AMA = \frac{500\ lb.}{50\ lb.} = 10$

$efficiency = \frac{AMA}{IMA} \cdot 100\%$

$efficiency = \frac{10}{15} \cdot 100\% = 66\frac{2}{3}\%$

15. $heat = (L_f)m + m(C)(\Delta t)$

$= (25\ \frac{kcal}{kg})(2\ kg) +$

$(2\ kg)(0.6)(100°C)$

$= 50\ kcal + 120\ kcal$

$= 170\ kcal$

16. total energy = PE + KE + heat

$20\ J = mgh + \frac{1}{2}mv^2 + heat$

$20\ J = (2\ kg)(9.8\ \frac{m}{sec.^2})(0.1\ m) +$

$\frac{1}{2}(2\ kg)(4\ \frac{m}{sec.})^2 + heat$

$= 1.96\ kg \cdot \frac{m^2}{sec.^2} +$

$16\ kg \cdot \frac{m^2}{sec.^2} + heat$

$20\ J = 17.96\ J + heat$

$heat = 20\ J - 17.96\ J$

$heat = 2\ J\ (approximately)$

191

1. h

2. k

3. a

4. b

5. g

6. c

7. e

8. d

9. f

10. i

11. c

12. b

13. c

14. a

15. d

16. **a**

17. b

18. d

19. a

20. c

21. $v = 330 \frac{m}{sec.} + (.6)(T) \frac{m}{sec.}$

$= 330 \frac{m}{sec.} + (.6)(10°) \frac{m}{sec.}$

$v = 336 \frac{m}{sec.}$

22. The unknown fork produces more than four beats when struck with the 505-Hz fork. The unknown fork, therefore, must have a frequency higher than the 510-Hz fork. 510 Hz + 4 Hz = 514 Hz

23.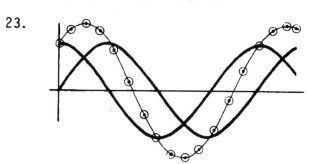

24. $v = f\lambda$

$\lambda = \frac{v}{f}$

$= \frac{3 \times 10^8 \frac{m}{sec.}}{9 \cdot 10^5 \ Hz}$

$= 333 \ m$

25. $T = \frac{1}{f} = \frac{1}{5 \ Hz} = 0.2 \ sec.$

1. k

2. j

3. c

4. i

5. h

6. f

7. g

8. a

9. e

10. d

11. true

12. true

13. false

14. false

15. true

16. b

17. d

18. c

19. a

20. b

21. $n = \frac{c}{v}$

$1.4 = \frac{3 \cdot 10^8 \frac{m}{sec.}}{v}$

$v = \frac{3 \cdot 10^8 \frac{m}{sec.}}{1.4}$

$v = 2.1 \cdot 10^8 \frac{m}{sec.}$

22.

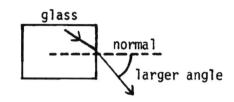

23.

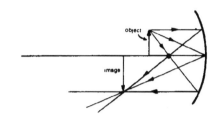

24. The image is real, inverted, and enlarged.

25.

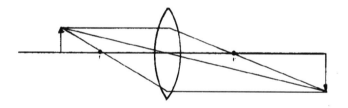

26. The image is real, inverted, and enlarged.

1. false

2. true

3. true

4. false

5. false

6. true

7. true

8. false

9. true

10. true

11. work

12. charged

13. magnetic

14. current

15. capacitence

16. b

17. b

18. c

19. c

20. d

21. a. The charge on the plates is reversed (the plate connected to the negative battery terminal is negatively charged.)

    b. The field vectors describe the direction of the force on positive test charges. These field vectors are reversed.

c. $E = \dfrac{12 \text{ v}}{0.4 \text{ cm}} = 30 \dfrac{\text{v}}{\text{cm}}$

d. $E = 30 \dfrac{\text{v}}{\text{cm}} = \dfrac{F}{q}$

    $F = 30 \text{ N}$

(any answer is acceptable that is numerically equivalent to part C)

22. a. The lines of force surrounding the left sphere should point away from the sphere. (or) The charges on the left sphere should be negative.

    b. upward (or) toward the top of the paper

1. true

2. true

3. false

4. false

5. false

6. false

7. true

8. true

9. false

10. true

11. f

12. a

13. d

14. a

15. j

16. g

17. h

18. b

19. e

20. a

21. a. $R_T = 10\Omega + 5\Omega = 15\Omega$

    b. $I = \dfrac{E}{R_T} = \dfrac{15 \text{ v}}{15\,\Omega} = 1$ **amp**

    c. Current is constant in a series circuit. $I = 1$ amp

    d. $V = IR_1 = (1 \text{ amp})(10\Omega)$
        $= 10$ volts

    e. $V = IR_2 = (1 \text{ amp})(5\Omega)$
        $= 5$ volts

    f. $P = E \cdot I = (15 \ V)(1 \text{ amp})$
        $= 15$ watts
        or
      $P = I^2 R_T = (1 \text{ amp})^2(15\Omega)$
        $= 15$ watts
        or
      $P = \dfrac{E^2}{R_T} = \dfrac{(15 \ V)^2}{15\Omega} = 15$ watts

22. a. $\dfrac{1}{R_T} = \dfrac{1}{3\Omega} + \dfrac{1}{9\Omega} = \dfrac{3}{9\Omega} + \dfrac{1}{9\Omega}$
        $= \dfrac{4}{9\Omega}$

      $R_T = \dfrac{9}{4}\Omega$ or $2\tfrac{1}{4}\Omega$

    b. $I = \dfrac{E}{R_T} = \dfrac{24 \ V}{2\tfrac{1}{4}\Omega} = 10.7$ amps

    c. $I = \dfrac{E}{R_1} = \dfrac{24 \ V}{3\Omega} = 8$ amps

    d. $I_2 = \dfrac{E}{R_2} = \dfrac{24 \ V}{9\Omega} = 2.7$ amps

    e. $V_{R_1} = E = 24 \ V$

    f. $P_1 = E \cdot I_1 = (24 \ V)(8 \text{ amps})$
        $= 192$ watts

1. d

2. e

3. a

4. f

5. c

6. true

7. false

8. true

9. false

10. false

11. false

12. true

13. true

14. true

15. true

16. b

17. a

18. c

19. b

20. b

21. b

22. d

23. b

24. d

25. d

26. Either order:
   a. electric or electrostatic fields
   b. magnetic fields

27. Either order:
   a. generator
   b. transformer

1. false
2. true
3. false
4. false
5. true
6. true
7. false
8. true
9. true
10. true
11. b
12. c
13. c
14. a
15. d
16. c
17. d
18. a
19. c
20. a
21. b
22. d
23. c
24. b

25. $mvr = \frac{nh}{2\pi}$

$v = \frac{nh}{2\pi\,mr}$

$= \dfrac{(5)(6.63 \times 10^{-34}\ \text{j}\cdot\text{sec.})}{(2)(3.14)(9.1 \times 10^{-31}\ \text{kg})(\frac{26.5}{2} \times 10^{-10}\ \text{m})}$

$= 0.0438 \cdot 10^{7}\ \frac{\text{m}}{\text{sec.}}$

$C = \pi d = (26.5 \times 10^{-10}\ \text{m})(3.14)$
$\quad C = 83.2 \times 10^{-10}\ \text{m}$

$\dfrac{1}{t} = \dfrac{v}{c} = \dfrac{0.0438 \times 10^{7}\ \frac{\text{m}}{\text{sec.}}}{83.2 \times 10^{-10}\ \text{m}}$

$= \dfrac{4.38 \times 10^{5}\ \frac{\text{m}}{\text{sec.}}}{83.2 \times 10^{-10}\ \text{m}}$

$= 0.0526 \times 10^{15}/\text{sec.}$
$= 5.26 \times 10^{13}\ \text{Hz}$

26 a. orbits are circular with balanced forces;
b. quantized orbits integers wavelengths;
c. energy exchange only allowed on orbit change

197

1.	f		28.	false
2.	a		29.	false
3.	k		30.	false
4.	g		31.	false
5.	j		32.	false
6.	b		33.	true
7.	d		34.	true
8.	e		35.	false
9.	i		36.	true
10.	c		37.	true
11.	j		38.	false
12.	e		39.	false
13.	a		40.	false
14.	h		41.	true
15.	c		42.	true
16.	b		43.	false
17.	i		44.	true
18.	f		45.	false
19.	d		46.	false
20.	g		47.	true
21.	false		48.	false
22.	true		49.	false
23.	true		50.	true
24.	true		51.	true
25.	false		52.	d
26.	true		53.	b
27.	true			

54. c

55. a

56. b

57. a

58. a

59. a

60. d

61. c

62. **b**

63. b

64. c

65. b

66. a

67. **b**

68. a

69. b

70. **a**

71. c

72. a.

1 proton	=	1.007593	amu
2 neutrons	=	+ 2.017964	amu
		3.025557	amu
1 triton	=	− 3.016448	amu
mass defect	=	0.009109	amu

b. $(0.009109 \text{ amu})(931 \frac{Mev}{amu}) =$
8.48 Mev

73. $i = \dfrac{\text{velocity of light in vacuum}}{\text{velocity of light in glass}}$

$1.5 = \dfrac{3 \cdot 10^8 \frac{m}{sec.}}{v}$

$v = \dfrac{3 \cdot 10^8 \frac{m}{sec.}}{1.5} = 2 \cdot 10^8 \frac{m}{sec.}$

74.

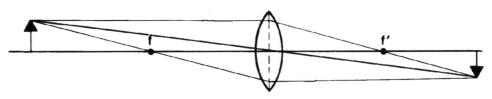

1. a

2. e

3. b

4. f

5. d

6. g

7. s = 50 mph

8. $a = \dfrac{5 \text{ m}}{\text{sec.}^2}$

9. a. .2 cm x .2 cm x .2 cm
    b. $V = 8 \times 10^{-3} \text{ cm}^3$ or .008 cm^3
    c. $8 \times 10^{-3} \text{ cm}^3$
    d. $\dfrac{\text{volume (substance)}}{\text{volume (molecule)}}$ = number of molecules
    e. 5×10^{17} molecules

10. $D = \dfrac{3g}{\text{cm}^3}$

11. D = 0

12. $10 \dfrac{\text{m}}{\text{sec.}}$

13. You can describe a temperature field by using a thermometer for readings. You would have to take readings for several years at different seasons to get an average pattern for each season of the year and this pattern would only be an average result.

14. The advantage is that it is simple and round and the child can understand. A disadvantage is that it does not show mountains, clouds, seasons, oceans, and so is limiting understanding.

1. e

2. a

3. b

4. d

5. f

6. g

7. $13 \dfrac{m}{sec.}$

8. $a = \dfrac{4\pi^2 R}{T^2} = \dfrac{4(3.14)^2(10\ m)}{(25)^2} = 98.6 \dfrac{m}{sec.}$

9. $\dfrac{R_A^{\,3}}{T_A^{\,2}} = \dfrac{R_B^{\,3}}{T_B^{\,2}} \qquad \dfrac{R_A^{\,3}}{(year)^2} = \dfrac{(4\ AU)^3}{(8\ year)^2} = \dfrac{64\ AU^3}{64\ year^2} \qquad R_A^{\,3} = 1\ AU^3 \qquad R_A = 1\ AU$

10. $d = v_0 t - \tfrac{1}{2}gt$

    $= (-15 \dfrac{ft.}{sec.})(2\ sec.) - \tfrac{1}{2}(32 \dfrac{ft.}{sec.^2})(2\ sec.)^2$

    $d = -30\ ft. - 64\ ft. = -94\ ft. = 94\ ft.$ down

11. $F = ma = (3\ kg)(15 \dfrac{m}{sec.^2}) = 45\ N$

    $F = 45\ N = ma = (1\ kg)(a) = 45 \dfrac{m}{sec.^2}$

12. $\qquad m_1 v_1 = m_2 v_2 + m_3 v_3$

    $(5\ kg)(6 \dfrac{m}{sec.}) = (2\ kg)(3 \dfrac{m}{sec.}) + (3\ kg)v_3$

    $30\ kg \cdot \dfrac{m}{sec.} = 6\ kg \dfrac{m}{sec.} + 3\ kg\ V_3$

    $3\ kg\ V_3 = 24\ kg \dfrac{m}{sec.}$

    $V_3 = 8 \dfrac{m}{sec.}$

13. The centripetal force of the road on the tires becomes zero because on ice friction is minimized.

14. $F = \dfrac{Gm_1m_2}{R^2}$ Although a larger radius does yield a smaller F, the mass of the sun is so much greater that F is large also.

15. $F = \dfrac{Gm_1m_2}{R^2}$ Since the diameters and therefore the radii are the same, the larger mass produces the larger force.

1. a

2. c

3. b

4. f

5. g

6. j

7. i

8. h

9. k

10. d

11. $E = P.E. + K.E$

$$= mgh + \tfrac{1}{2}mv^2$$

$$= (4 \text{ kg})(9.8 \tfrac{m}{sec.})(25 \text{ m}) + \tfrac{1}{2}(4 \text{ kg})(5 \tfrac{m}{sec.})^2$$

$$E = 980 \text{ kg} \cdot \tfrac{m^2}{s^2} + 50 \text{ kg} \cdot \tfrac{m^2}{sec.^2}$$

$$= 1{,}030 \text{ kg} \cdot \tfrac{m^2}{sec.^2} = 1{,}030 \text{ j}$$

12. $P = \dfrac{E}{t} = \dfrac{mgh}{t}$

$$= \frac{(5 \text{ kg})(9.8 \tfrac{m}{sec.})(100 \text{ m})}{5 \text{ sec.}}$$

$$= \frac{980 \text{ kg} \cdot \tfrac{m^2}{sec.^2}}{sec.} = 980 \tfrac{j}{sec.} = 980 \text{ W}$$

13. $P.E. = K.E.$

$$mgh = \tfrac{1}{2}mv^2$$

$$(2 \text{ sl})(32 \tfrac{ft.}{sec.})(h) = \tfrac{1}{2}(2 \text{ sl})(8 \tfrac{ft.}{sec.})^2$$

$$h = \frac{64 \text{ sl} \tfrac{ft.^2}{sec.^2}}{64 \text{ sl} \tfrac{ft.^2}{sec.^2}} = 1 \text{ ft.}$$

14. $\text{IMA} = \dfrac{30 \text{ in.}}{2 \text{ in.}} = 15$

$\text{AMA} = \dfrac{200 \text{ lb.}}{20 \text{ lb.}} = 10$

$\text{Efficiency} = \dfrac{\text{AMA}}{\text{IMA}} \cdot 100\% = \dfrac{10}{15} \cdot 100\% = 66.66\%$

15. $\text{H.E.} = m \cdot L_v + m(\text{sp. ht.}) \, \Delta t$

$= (2 \text{ kg})(204 \, \dfrac{\text{kcal}}{\text{kg}}) + (2 \text{ kg})(0.6)(50°C)$

$= 408 \text{ kcal} + \text{kcal}$

$= 468 \text{ kcal}$

16. $E = \text{P.E.} + \text{K.E.} + \text{H.E.}$

$100 \, \dfrac{\text{ft.}}{\text{lb.}} = mgh + \tfrac{1}{2}mv^2 + \text{H.E.}$

$= (\tfrac{1}{2} \text{ sl})(32 \, \dfrac{\text{ft.}}{\text{sec.}^2})(2 \text{ ft}) + \tfrac{1}{2}(\tfrac{1}{2} \text{ sl})(8 \, \dfrac{\text{ft.}}{\text{sec.}})^2 + \text{H.E.}$

$= 64 \text{ sl} \, \dfrac{\text{ft.}^2}{\text{sec.}^2} + 16 \text{ sl} \, \dfrac{\text{ft.}^2}{\text{sec.}^2} + \text{H.E.}$

$\text{H.E.} = 100 \, \dfrac{\text{ft.}}{\text{lb.}} - 64 \, \dfrac{\text{ft.}}{\text{lb.}} - 16 \, \dfrac{\text{ft.}}{\text{lb.}}$

$= 20 \, \dfrac{\text{ft.}}{\text{lb.}}$

1. a

2. f

3. b

4. e

5. d

6.

7.

8. $v = f\lambda$

$$f = \frac{v}{\lambda}$$

$$f = \frac{3 \cdot 10^8 \;\frac{m}{sec.}}{6 \cdot 10^{-7} \; m} = 5 \cdot 10^{14} \; Hz$$

9. $v = 330 + (.6)(^\circ C) \dfrac{m}{sec.}$

$$= 330 + (.6)(10) \frac{m}{sec.}$$

$$= 336 \; \frac{m}{sec.}$$

10. $\dfrac{(n - \frac{1}{2})\lambda}{d} = \dfrac{X}{L}$ $\dfrac{(2 - \frac{1}{2})\lambda}{3 \; cm} = \dfrac{9 \; cm}{18 \; cm}$ $\dfrac{\frac{3}{2}\lambda}{3 \; cm} = \dfrac{1}{2}$ $3\lambda = 3 \; cm$

$$\lambda = 1 \; cm$$

11. 510 Hz – 5 = 505 Hz
     510 Hz + 5 = 515 Hz
     505 Hz – 10 = 495 Hz
     505 Hz + 10 = 515 Hz
          unknown = 515 Hz

12. A wave in a low velocity medium approaches a boundary at the critical angle or greater and is completely reflected.

13. Diffraction is the bending of a wave in the same medium. Refraction is the bending of a wave as it passes from one medium to another.

14. If all the feet hit the bridge at the same time, the energy is imparted rhythmically. If the steps are at the natural frequency of the bridge, the bridge will resonate and vibrations will always result.

1. f

2. e

3. d

4. a

5. c

6. g

7. The image is real, diminished, and inverted.

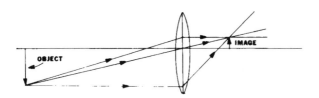

8. $\dfrac{x}{L} = \dfrac{\lambda}{w}$ $2 \text{ mm} = 2 \cdot 10^{-3} \text{ m}$

$\dfrac{2 \cdot 10^{-3} \text{ m}}{1 \text{ m}} = \dfrac{6 \cdot 10^{-7} \text{ m}}{w}$ $w = \dfrac{6 \cdot 10^{-7} \text{ m}}{2 \cdot 10^{-3}}$ $w = 3 \cdot 10^{-4} \text{ m} = 0.3 \text{ mm}$

9. $S_o S_i = f$ $\dfrac{H_o}{H_i} = \dfrac{S_o}{f}$ $2H_i = 8 \text{ cm}$

$(24 \text{ cm})(6 \text{ cm}) = f$ $H_i = 4 \text{ cm}$

$f = 144 \text{ cm}$ $\dfrac{8 \text{ cm}}{H_i} = \dfrac{24 \text{ cm}}{12 \text{ cm}}$

$f = 12 \text{ cm}$

10. $n = \dfrac{c}{v}$

$= \dfrac{3 \cdot 10^8 \;\frac{m}{\text{sec.}}}{1.5 \cdot 10^8 \;\frac{m}{\text{sec.}}} = 2$

11.

air
water
smaller angle

12. Interference is a two-slit experiment and diffraction is a one-slit phenomenon. Taylor used diffraction to demonstrate the particle nature of light.

13. In refraction of particles, the rolling balls did not behave the way light does. Taylor's diffraction experiment showed that light decreased and acted as a particle.

1. a

2. b

3. d

4. b

5. b

6. c

7. a

8. c

9. c

10. d

11. a. $W = \frac{1}{2}CV^2$
    b. four times
    c. $C = \dfrac{Q}{V}$
    d. charge

12. a. continuous
    b. electric current

1. true

2. false

3. false

4. true

5. true

6. true

7. true

8. false

9. true

10. true

11. 0.5

12. 24

13. 1.5

14. 2.5

15. 2.0

16. 3

17. 2

18. 1

19. 4

20. 144

1. true

2. true

3. false

4. true

5. false

6. false

7. true

8. false

9. true

10. true

11. conductor

12. moved

13. current

14. electromotive force

15. transformer

16. force

17. bar magnet

18. solenoidal

19. opposite

20. vector

21. electron

22. Either order:
    a. electric
    b. magnetic

23. cathode

24. brightness

25. a. charge
    b. mass

1. false

2. false

3. true

4. true

5. true

6. true

7. true

8. true

9. true

10. true

11. b

12. c

13. b

14. b

15. c

16. energy

17. quanta

18. Either order:
    a. position
    b. momentum

19. quantum

20. neutrons

21. a. line
    b. continuous

22. momentum

23. electrostatic

24. $7.3 \cdot 10^{-9}$ M

25. 10 ev

1. k

2. f

3. i

4. g

5. b

6. c

7. d

8. a

9. e

10. h

11. d

12. b

13. a

14. b

15. c

16. b

17. b

18. d

19. a

20. b

21. g

22. i

23. f

24. a

25. d

26. b

27. c

28. k

29. h

30. e

31. $c = f\lambda$

$$f = \frac{3 \cdot 10^8 \ \frac{m}{sec.}}{4 \cdot 10^{-7} \ \frac{m}{sec.}} = 7.5 \cdot 10^{14} \ Hz$$

32. $n = \frac{c}{v} = \dfrac{3 \cdot 10^8 \ \frac{m}{sec.}}{2.0 \cdot 10^8 \ \frac{m}{sec.}} = 1.5$

33.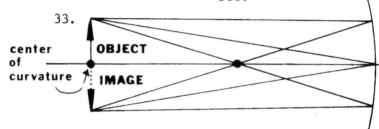

34. 3 cm because the object is at the center of curvature